CLAIM TO FREEDOM

The Rise of the Afro-Asian Peoples

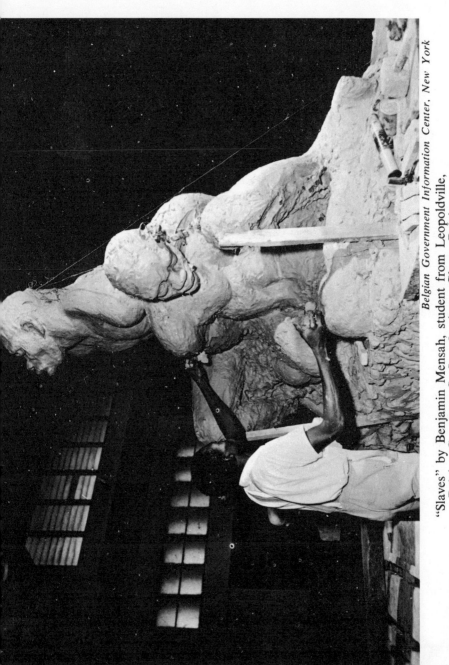

Belgian Government Information Center, New York

"Slaves" by Benjamin Mensah, student from Leopoldville,
Belgian Congo, at St. Luc Institute, Ghent, Belgium

Claim
to Freedom

The Rise
of the Afro-Asian Peoples

Cornelia Spencer

Illustrated

The John Day Company, New York

Books by Cornelia Spencer

Three Sisters
China Trader
Elizabeth: England's Modern Queen
The Exile's Daughter
The Land of the Chinese People
Made in China
Made in India
The Missionary
Nehru of India
Straight Furrow
Understanding the Japanese
Seven Thousand Islands
Romulo: Voice of Freedom
The Song in the Streets
More Hands for Man
Claim to Freedom

Library of Congress Catalogue Card Number: 62-7781

Foreword

The purpose of this book is to view the spirit of freedom at work in the world. It can give no more than a glimpse, as through a telescope which sweeps the horizon and so cannot be focused for closer points at the same time. It is intended to seek out the panorama of growing independence among the people of Africa and Asia, rather than the events of their history themselves, and the lens is so set.

The record of rising independence is not one of color or race, of East or West. Slave has longed for freedom from master, clan has fought to throw off rival clan, nation has subjected nation, and empires have risen and fallen in both hemispheres, through the ages. Individual countries have demanded change of government within their own borders by civil wars and revolutions.

Many factors have gone into the development of each large group of the human race; each is affected by them without choice. Location with respect to oceans and currents, topography, climates, and perhaps most of all, natural resources have had a great deal to do with the history of nations. But now the spirit of freedom is everywhere, in everything, for, in the end, man's own will is the greatest historical factor of all.

Today the mood of independence is so widespread, the movement to become modern so swift and powerful that large sections of the world's people seem to be rising out of the past and leaping toward the future. A telescope has to swing sharply to catch even a glimpse of all that is taking place. It cannot tarry for background, nor can it see through to what is to come. Its lens, also, may all too easily take on a shade that is too rosy or too dark, perhaps in part because of the contrasts that it finds. It dare not be hoped that that such a broad view of stirring people as this book attempts will be without distortions. Even the clearest mirror distorts to some degree. But if the reader feels the living power of freedom, sees some of the reasons for its new strength, realizes the part that a longing for modernization and a more comfortable life plays in countries of great ancient civilizations, the book will have served its purpose.

Every country in the world is involved in what is going on today. Each has been, or is, or will be responsible for a part in the drama of freedom. It cannot be otherwise, for it is the story of mankind's aspirations, and no one will deny his kinship to the family of man.

CLAIM TO FREEDOM

The Rise of the Afro-Asian Peoples

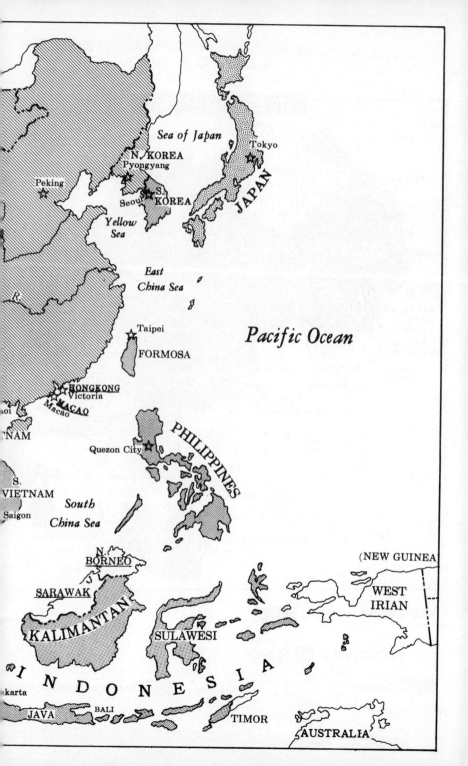

AFRICA

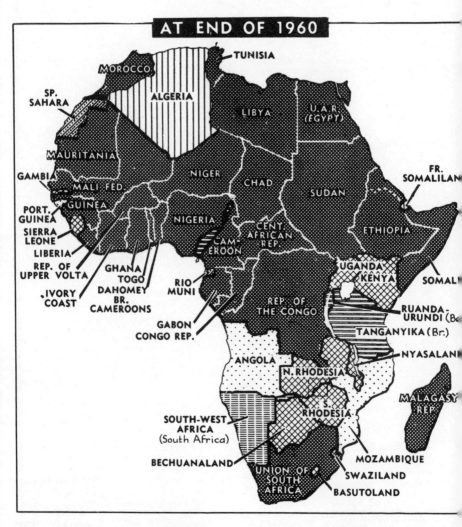

AT END OF 1960

MOROCCO
TUNISIA
SP. SAHARA
ALGERIA
LIBYA
U.A.R. (EGYPT)
MAURITANIA
FR. SOMALILAN
GAMBIA
MALI FED.
NIGER
CHAD
SUDAN
PORT. GUINEA
GUINEA
ETHIOPIA
SIERRA LEONE
NIGERIA
CENT. AFRICAN REP.
LIBERIA
CAMEROON
REP. OF UPPER VOLTA
GHANA
TOGO
DAHOMEY
BR. CAMEROONS
RIO MUNI
UGANDA
KENYA
SOMAL
IVORY COAST
RUANDA-URUNDI (Be
GABON
CONGO REP.
REP. OF THE CONGO
TANGANYIKA (Br.)
NYASALAN
ANGOLA
N. RHODESIA
MALAGASY REP.
SOUTH-WEST AFRICA (South Africa)
S. RHODESIA
BECHUANALAND
MOZAMBIQUE
SWAZILAND
UNION OF SOUTH AFRICA
BASUTOLAND

INDEPENDENT NATIONS

 U. N. Trusteeship

DEPENDENCIES: British [[[[[French

 Spanish  Portuguese 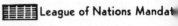 League of Nations Mandat

Courtesy the N.Y. Ti

CHAPTER 1

C HANDRA'S eye caught the Hong Kong stamp and postmark on a letter he was about to put into its proper box. It made him feel again the excitement and adventure that handling mail from all over the world brought, as he sorted it each day. It reminded him of his childhood, too.

It was summer, 1959. He had had his position as a mail clerk in the post office of Nairobi, capital of Kenya, East Africa, for only a few weeks. Often, looking out on Delamere Avenue, when there was time to pause, he could scarcely believe that he had finished school and was here at work. He was proud of the modern city with its many tall buildings. The avenue was lined with trees and was said to be as beautiful as any in the world. He visualized Nairobi not only as a fine city but as a point where far-reaching lines of communication between islands and continent crossed.

Not only had it been hard for him to learn the

11

location of thousands of individual boxes so that he could sort quickly; it was often difficult to decipher the handwriting of the addresses. They might have been written by Arabs, Turks, Japanese, Chinese or others who were not used to the English alphabet. This resulted in strange scripts and odd mistakes. If they were written in languages other than English or his native Hindi, he had to go to others for help.

Nairobi had no mail delivery system. This meant that letters were sorted and stowed in boxes to be claimed by residents or their servants and made the post office a kind of general meeting place. This was true even though the boxes were not in the main building but in a separate one. People were constantly coming to the mail windows of the central lobby to ask questions, buy stamps, or fetch mail which was held there for visitors or for special reasons.

Chandra would have liked to spend time simply watching the many kinds of people who came and went, for Delamere Avenue was full of color and variety. But he had no time for this. He had to learn greater and greater speed and efficiency.

Yet the letter from Hong Kong interrupted his attention to his work. It reminded him instantly of his father. He remembered in a flash the times they had sat together on the high veranda at the back of their house on Jevanjee Street. There his father had often talked about India and China, and about men from the West who had gone to the Far East. Hong Kong, the British East India Company in India and then in China, treaties, colonialism, restrictions on trade, special rights for Europeans—all came to mind when he thought of his father.

For Sudar Mookerji had known a great deal about all this even though he could never have been called an educated man. It did not take much schooling to learn that Portuguese had tried to get footholds in the Orient through trade in spices and by religious invasion, or that Dutch and then Spanish and British people had pushed them aside to claim what they had won. Britain had come to dominate almost all of India, first commerically and then politically, while she developed trading centers in China, as well. The story of her relationship to Australia and New Zealand had followed her successes in India. There was also the record of how she had come to Africa!

But today the time was near noon and the sun was searing hot on the glistening street beyond the doors. The altitude of 5,452 feet, however, would make the air chill and fresh by dusk. Remembrance deepened in Chandra's mind as he went on through the letters in his hand, putting each in its proper box. The real meaning of what his father had so often talked about had come to him more clearly as he grew up.

For Chandra's father, Sudar Mookerji, had studied the past until no one could fault him on a point of information. He had needed no prompting on how the West had invaded the Far East and the "Dark Continent" as the English textbooks often referred to Africa. He had been a small man, dark brown in color. His straight, black hair had grown low and thick on his brow. His deep-set eyes had seemed to

13

burn below an overhanging forehead. He had always been restless, forever moving his hands which were slender and agile. He had been a tailor by profession, and sitting cross-legged on his mat he had designed and sewn the finest of imported woolen suits for those who wanted western dress. By some sixth sense he had seemed to know how to cut without patterns, guided by feeling rather than reason. One day he was going to have his shop in the Bazaar, beside other business houses; they would move to a wealthier residence section as Allidina Visram and Suliman Virjee had done.

Meantime he worked hard, but, while his hands moved cleverly, his active mind was gathering information wherever it could. The fact that his own parents were Indians who had come to Africa, though before his birth, had kept him always a little outside of what was going on in Nairobi, or even in East Africa. He had never for a moment forgotten that he was Indian.

As a boy, Chandra had worshipped his father and had sat watching him and listening to him by the hour. When he was old enough to go to school, he had always rushed home from the little Indian school he attended, to report the events of the day. His father had given him grave attention.

Though the frail-looking tailor had been lively and energetic, he lost his life in an epidemic. He was alive and well one day and dead the next.

Thinking of all this today, Chandra found his throat tight, for he had loved his father very much . . . Sudar had been a descendant of the Indians whom the British had brought to Kenya to work for them because they said the local Africans were not satisfactory. The white men had complained that the "natives" did not seem to understand what it meant to "stay by" one's word. Nothing, it seemed, could be as important as a village festival or a tribal initiation which might mean staying away for a full cycle of the moon since much of the social life was timed to the moon. Uninterested in studying the people, the British pioneers were simply in search of workers, and, not finding them in Africa, they had brought them across the Indian Ocean . . . But Sudar had learned not to let himself think too much about the distant past. He knew that here in Kenya his people had come to be known for their efficiency and cleverness; they were often envied, or even hated, by Africans.

Chandra had just finished the sorting and returned to the main building, when he noticed a small group that was entering the lobby. He felt sure that they must be Americans. Their very variety underscored his opinion, for among them was a boy so dark that he must have African origins; a girl so fair that she could only be Scandinavian; a Japanese or a Japanese-American. They were all talking and laughing together—but one was not surprised at anything that arrived from the United States of America.

Chandra watched while they went to the mail window to ask questions of the clerk stationed there. They seemed free and easy in manner and unconscious of everyone around them.

One tall boy leaned on the sill and peered at the

15

clerk. "Anything here for James Smith?" he demanded in a drawling voice. "Or," he went on, "for Alice Svenson, or for Peter Hope, or for Cecilia Anton, or for William Miamoto?" He turned and grinned over his shoulder at the others who had lined up behind him. "That'll be enough to throw him for a while," he said, as if expecting the clerk to understand some things he said and not others.

The short Indian clerk turned away from the window

Delamere Avenue, Nairobi, Kenya, named for the British pioneer whose statue can be seen.

to search the pigeon holes in the back. He returned with a handful of letters, and watched as they were distributed among the group. Such a party could only come from America. Here in Nairobi people did not mix like that. The African had his place, the Indian his, and the European his. That was the way things worked best. After all, should Africans step over into Indian positions? For generations his ancestors had been clerks, even though they had been builders when the British had brought them over—just as Chandra's people had been laborers before they took up tailoring.

He and Chandra had once discussed the new ideas some Africans seemed to be getting. They were unreasonable, they decided. If one didn't like what the British had done, one could go even further back and talk about the early Arab trade in African slaves. It had been so inhuman that the English traders claimed that one reason for their coming had been to put an end to the monstrous cruelty of the Arabs. However one wanted to interpret that part of history, the two young men had concluded that each race had its place.

Now here came a group made up of all kinds of people! The clerk at the window watched while the young people tore their letters open and read them as they stood there in the lobby, sharing bits of news.

Chandra, in the room behind, his hands again full of letters, watched, too. Why were these young people so different from those here in Nairobi? For people in this city behaved in all sorts of unusual ways. Still, there were some lines that were never crossed. These were the color lines, which were also social lines. It

17

was almost as though someone had taken a piece of chalk and marked the city into sections—one for Europeans and Americans, one for Indians, one for Africans, one for Somalis. Somaliland lay along the sea coast to the north and east of Kenya. Its people were nomadic Mohammedans, of Arabic origins. They were dignified, loved rich tapestries and hangings; got on well with the Africans if the question of equality was never raised.

The sections of Nairobi had nothing whatever to do with education or family background. It was a question of blood. Why, the part of the city where Chandra had lived as a boy—and still lived because of his father's early death—was almost like a part of India itself. All the street signs, though written in English, announced Indian tradesmen or craftsmen, just as his father's sign had read, SUDAR MOOKERJI, FINE TAILORING. This was true even along the Bazaar, for important trade was in the hands of Indians. People who came and went along the streets always wore their Sikh turbans or their Hindu sari.

Chandra stepped forward to take his place at the window now that he had finished sorting for a time. It was hard not to half-hear some of the chatter of the young Americans, even though other people were coming and going.

"Listen to this from an old friend of mine," the tall fellow who had asked for the mail said, reading aloud as the others stood a little to one side. " 'Folks in your part of town had a meeting about renting or selling to Negroes. A lot of young people home for the sum-

18

mer were there. They're going out after Negro families who'll be willing to come, and then help every way they can. Everyone saw that this was necessary if we are to have real school integration and open public services. It was great!' I half-wish I were there instead of here," James Smith said slowly, folding the letter.

"And miss the international conference at Makerere College?" someone demanded. "There'll be people from all over the world there."

Peter Hope, the only Negro member of the group, smiled, then glanced around to see who was noticing and so might have overheard the reading. He had not been sure for a long time that it was a good idea for him to attend the conference in Uganda, for he did not want to be an exhibit or a martyr. If he could be unnoticed, just one of the American delegation to Africa, it would be all right. Now he believed that this was the way it was going to be. No one here in Nairobi seemed to wonder about his presence. People here must be used to any kind of combinations coming in. The United States Department of State required that all American citizens be suitably lodged when they came to Kenya. In Nairobi certain hotels and the Y.M.C.A. were designated for such guests.

But the fact that these special arrangements had to be made and what he soon observed in the city made it clear to Peter that in Kenya his race brothers were thought of as belonging to the lowest social group. He had so hoped to find it less so than it was at home.

Now the enthusiastic Jim was reading eagerly from another letter. "Look at *this*," he exclaimed, throwing his arms across Peter's shoulder and drawing him closer. "You know, I believe that America *is* beginning to change, and it's we young ones that are going to make it." He pointed to lines on the page.

Peter· read, his eyes lighting in spite of habitual caution. "What great guys to get into it like that," he said softly, when he had finished. If his country could only lead the way toward equality of opportunity— but, instead, she was often pushed by other countries, he thought sadly.

He smoothed down his drip-dry shirt and tucked it in more neatly, glancing at the people who were standing near. No one except the clerk at the window was paying any attention to them. He was Indian, Peter saw, and he was clearly interested in what was going on among the Americans. He must have overheard some of what had been said, though his expression suggested no point of view.

When there was an opening, Peter stepped forward to speak to Chandra in a low voice. "I shall be getting letters from London," he said, "and will call for them in a few days. We shall all be getting mail . . . Perhaps you would like to get acquainted with our group," he added for Chandra's eyes had grown interested.

Peter's English, though touched with American pronunciations, was correct, Chandra noticed. It was clear that he was a student. But then, that was America for you. Anyone went to school and even on to university. He had rarely spoken to an African except to give orders, but now he smiled politely at Peter. "I shall watch for the letters and have them ready for you. Of course I should be pleased to know more about your group."

"I am Peter Hope," Peter murmured. "Behind me is James Smith, and—Jim, take it from there," he finished. He had learned by experience never to push personal friendship too far in a new situation.

At last everyone had been introduced, causing a good deal of impatience among the other people who were there on business. Chandra had learned that the group of young people were on their way to a conference in Uganda, but little more.

The Americans left the post office and stepped into the street. The late afternoon air was beginning to come in, deliciously fresh and invigorating. This place seemed to have everything—clubs, business houses, hotels, parks—as well as people from all over the world. Here, more than two hundred miles from the Indian Ocean where Arabs, Portuguese, and English had sailed back and forth with slaves and riches of the Far East, stood Nairobi, the city called "sweet water," built on the Athi Plains. Nearby lay Naivasha Lake where hippopotamuses and otters and flamingos liked to gather; near, also, stretched the beautiful Limuru coffee and tea plantations. The city itself had about 16,000 white people, 44,000 Indians, 109,000 black Africans more than half of whom belonged to the Kikuyu tribe. Along one edge stretched the great wild game park. In the city stood the famed Corindon Museum. Streets signs suggested contacts with Poland, Hungary, Italy, France as well as with India and England. Peter knew that only a few miles away in

Nomadic Masai warriors of Kenya, absorbed in their
first newspaper.

their own reserve lived the Masai, nomads whose food was milk and blood.

The group of Americans moved on quickly to the Y.M.C.A. They must have dinner and then attend a meeting.

In the post office, Chandra closed the drawers for which he was responsible, put pens, pencils, rubber stamps and other small, useful things away, pulled down the grill, locked it, and made ready for closing time. He still felt stirred up by the pleasant friendliness of the black American. He was sure that the lines between Africans and Indians were fixed and he had no wish to move them. Yet, an educated black man from the United States of America was somehow different.

As he started home, it occurred to him that it would be interesting to invite this group to his home. It would not seem astonishing since they *were* Americans. His younger brother, who was thirteen, would pepper them with questions; his mother would ply them all with her special dishes. If his father were still alive, he would have asked them grave, thoughtful questions—only, Chandra quickly reminded himself, he would not even have been thinking of inviting such a group to his home had Sudar Mookerji still been living. If there had been one basic idea that was clear and unchangeable in the small man's mind, it was that African and Indian had nothing whatsoever in common. No, he would certainly not have been dreaming as he was, if his father had been involved, but he had died, now long ago.

CHAPTER 2

"WHY not?" Chandra's mother said instantly the evening he asked her about inviting the Americans to their home. Her black eyes were sparkling when she turned them on him. Now that he was grown he sometimes wondered about her independence and open-mindedness. For Rosie Mookerji, though a short, heavy person, was bursting with activity. To this day she had never told her sons much about her childhood, but she had suggested that "blue" blood as well as Indian blood flowed in her veins.

"Well, you know how Americans are—all kinds of people thrown together," Chandra explained, growing uncomfortable. "Those of Scandinavian origins, of Asian origins, of African origins, and, I suppose of just mixed white origins, are among them."

"You are simply saying that not all of them are Asian or white," Rosie said, pulling the sari she wore more firmly into place over her shoulder. "Well, I

24

would say that they should be an interesting lot. Invite them."

Though he was so used to her and to her ways, Chandra had to smile—just as his father had smiled when he first discovered that her name was Rosie. He had thought that if her parents had been able to foresee what she would be like, they could not have found a name which suited her so perfectly. It seemed to come from anywhere but the Indian group of Nairobi and every time the small, stocky woman flung out her hands in quick constant gestures, each time she settled herself in her seat in a decisive sort of way, whenever her eyes flashed, "Rosie" seemed to have been created for her.

The Americans came one evening. Chandra, feeling that it was all rather like a dream, met them at the gate and invited them to come in, leading the way through a narrow passage to the door of the house. His home was not a villa on the edge of Nairobi, but it was comfortable and had a pleasant garden in the back.

When he introduced his mother and saw the pleased expressions on his guests' faces, he suddenly felt very proud of her. Yet, she was not speaking in the soft tones of most Indian women he knew. She was direct in her manner and, as always, eagerly interested in everything. He noticed that today she was wearing a string of large amber beads which he knew his father had given her. She had not had them on for a long time. Her sari was gay, full of reds and yellows and

25

browns. She was truly handsome as she came forward holding out both hands in warm welcome to the young people.

"Enter," she said merrily, "but only if you are prepared for many questions." She half turned and drew Chandra's brother forward by the hand. "This is Balamu who would rather be called Tom." She almost pushed him toward the group. "He won't say anything about himself, but he stands very high in his form during school." She flashed the boy a brilliant smile and then wheeled to lead the way into the central living room. The fragrances of curries and coffee were teasingly pleasant.

"Now then, I shall leave you to the young hosts and retire to the kitchen for a bit," she said. "I have no faith in the artistic touch of any servant," she added.

Soon they were all settled on couches, chairs or low stools. The girls looked around curiously, enjoying everything; the men were wondering what the evening's conversation would turn up.

It began slowly with remarks about the international aspects of the city. The young people all admitted that they had secretly thought that it would be more like coming to the jungle, even though they knew better. They found on comparing notes that they had thought it would be possible to refer to the people of Africa as a whole as the Africans, but that now they were beginning to see that there were no such people. In Nairobi they had already noticed a dozen different kinds of Africans and realized that there must be dozens more. It was certainly true that most Americans had no idea of the number of countries or of the number of different types of people on the great continent. There were besides the African peoples, two large groups—the Asians and the Europeans.

Willie Miamoto had an orderly mind which pigeon-holed facts easily. He had prepared himself for this trip. Now he could not keep from pointing out that Africa was four times as large as the United States, contained one fifth of the earth's surface, had a population of 198 million native people made up of three main groups but countless tribes speaking at least seven hundred main languages, and that it had fifty-four countries or political divisions. He had to laugh at the astonished expression on the faces of his friends as they listened to his recital. "And there are about five million white people," he added as a postscript.

Jim grinned at the Japanese-American in an annoying kind of way and remarked that all he had reported so carefully would be out of date almost at once. Willie gave him a short nod in reply.

Cecilia wondered aloud why Nairobi was so different from Algiers. She had been to Algeria once and it had seemed very French except for the fact that there were many Arab people there. But of course it was part of what used to be French North Africa. As she spoke, her voice took on a touch of pride. This was too much for Alice.

"All I can say is that you are talking more like a

27

French person than like an American," she said abruptly. " 'French North Africa' you say, as though it could ever rightly have belonged to France!"

"The French have been in Algeria since 1830," Cecilia insisted in a low voice.

"Then why are there so many Arabs there?"

"It's in Arab country, you could say," Cecilia persisted, "but the civilization is French. Of course some day Algeria will demand independence just as Morocco and Tunisia did—still they are as French as French." She broke off, but her thoughts went on. There had been French West Africa, French Equatorial Africa and Madagascar, too.

The rest of the group were astonished at the exchange between the girls. Yet they realized that Cecilia had reasons for her feeling about France. France was certainly not the only country that had been interested in Africa. British holdings were scattered all over the continent, but its rule was usually described as "beneficent" or "looking toward independence" in modern times. Anyone who looked at any map could see that Egypt, the Sudan, Uganda and Kenya, the Rhodesias, Nyasaland, the Union of South Africa, Nigeria, Gold Coast, or Ghana, and Sierra Leone had all been British-controlled at the time of the First World War.

Of course that was a long time ago. What mattered now was how fast things were being changed so that people controlled their own countries; how fast they were taking their proper places in the modern world.

28

French Embassy Press and Information Division, New York

Modern Algiers, twin sister to Marseilles.

Everyone ought to be glad when a people stepped forward and asked to be free of colonial rule, and announced its readiness to take care of itself.

This was happening, for, while it was true that Britain had once held so many parts of Africa, the fact was that during the coming year, in 1960, the Rhodesias and Sierra Leone were going to be the only ones left that Britain had anything to say about, except for Uganda and Kenya. The United Nations would be her spokesman from then on. No one could deny that that was real progress.

But Cecilia, her eyes burning because she demanded fair play, was meantime thinking that France, too, was making progress in liberating colonies. By the end of 1960 only Algeria on the continent of Africa would be in her hands—and perhaps not even Algeria. One could not be sure what President de Gaulle was going to do.

In the middle of all this speculation and discussion, Willie sat smiling on everyone in his pleasant kind of way. He felt sure that all over the world people who were behind the times or who had been under colonial governments were just going to decide that they would have to manage their own affairs and catch up with the modern situation. Japan was a wonderful example. But of course not everyone was going to be happy at the changes this point of view would bring—not any more than are parents who hang around grown up children and want to continue to manage everything for them.

"I've heard a lot about France and England," Alice said, breaking a silence that had fallen on them for a little while, "but there's one spot in the heart of this continent that I've been told the most astonishing things about. That's the Belgian Congo. I think that it is the only part of Africa that Belgium has ever had, but she seems to have acquired it in a strange way." Alice's Scandinavian blondness seemed to glow in the darkening room.

"Before we go further, I shall fetch something cool to drink," Chandra said in his precise English. He felt smothered by the serious conversation and the spots of heavy, almost profound, silence. It seemed to him as though the world was being torn apart and analyzed in his very home; countries thrown about; empires judged. He had not expected these young people to feel so anxious about the world. But his courtesy held and he added apologetically, as he left the room, "My mother is an excellent chef, which means that she has not the slightest idea about time when she is creating food." He flashed them a smile and disappeared. Tom followed him silently.

In the pause that took place, the Americans heard a burst of chatter in the mother's voice and the boys' laughing replies. It made them wonder whether they had been friendly enough to their hosts.

Soon Tom and Chandra were back with glasses and bottled drinks. "The meal is almost ready," Chandra reported as he served them all. Perhaps then the talk would grow less serious, he thought.

31

There was no stopping the direction now. Jim started in again on the Belgian Congo. "I just don't think there is any way of understanding it," he announced. "None of us knows what is going to happen there. When those riots took place last January, Belgium promised independence in 1960. But one always hears that the people are not prepared for it. If it is granted suddenly, all kinds of things could happen. After all, a country that is seventy-seven times the size of its parent will take *some* educating for such a step. I've been told practically no one has had any higher education."

"Right," Willie put in. The others turned to him instinctively. Two or three chimed, "Go ahead, Willie. Fill us in." Even Chandra waited expectantly.

Willie listed the statistics briefly.

With 12 million people, the Belgian Congo had only about 1.8 persons to the square mile; Japan, by comparison, had 204. The country was about the size of India though India had approximately 356 million people.

"Nothing makes sense," Alice moaned. "In some places people are crowded together; in others they are so thinly scattered that they can scarcely find each other. I suppose a lot depends upon what there is to live on."

"And how they have used what they have," Willie added. He knew how hard the Japanese worked and how they made use of everything they had.

Jim considered the question of the Belgian Congo while he drank his cool drink thirstily. He was famished and the wonderful odors coming from the rear of the house were setting him wild. But he could not resist displaying some of his knowledge.

"The Congo has a long history of western man's bad behavior," he announced with the touch of a professor, setting down his empty glass. "I happen to have read a bit of history on that subject, but I refuse to display my knowledge now beyond saying that it was the work of Leopold II, King of the Belgians." But having so launched into the subject, Jim had to go on.

Leopold's rule began in 1865, only thirty-four years after Belgium itself became a country. He had been a man of expansive dreams and Africa was inviting. Even though he worked through what was called The Congo International Association, the same Henry Stanley who was associated with David Livingstone served as his agent and was his right hand man for four years. In that time the Congo became Leopold's private property because of treaties with African chiefs which Stanley signed for him, and because The Berlin Conference gave it to the Belgian king, calling it The Congo Free State. It was a fantastic bit of history.

"This story is not so different from that of other annexations of subject people or of what we are now calling under-developed people," Peter remarked in his quiet way. "Usually it has been done without so much publicity." He drank from his glass without looking at anyone.

"It was the beginning of one of the blackest records

33

of history," Jim began just as Rosie Mookerji appeared at the door.

"Dinner is ready, at last," she announced. "You must be half-starved. Ladies, we shall lead the way in the European fashion . . . No, no, Boro," she interrupted herself to say to the small black maid. "Don't put it there but in the center of the table." The girl smiled broadly and set the bowl where she was told to set it and ran quickly out, flashing eyes and teeth at the guests.

Obeying the swift instructions of their hostess's hands, everyone was soon seated comfortably around the table. This inner room was hung with warm-colored velvets and tapestries. The fragrances of spice were strong.

Peter watched his hostess, fascinated. Her friendly joviality reminded him so much of his own mother. She had had the same freshness and cheerfulness about her.

Rosie passed the various dishes and saw that each person took an ample helping. Boro trotted around trying to please her mistress. She seemed to be having as much fun as anyone else, and if she was failing to do as well as Rosie expected, there was no sign of her displeasure now.

"Watch the curry in that bowl there," Rosie cautioned, indicating a particular one. She always ground and mixed her own, for curries were really combinations of many spices and there was no such thing as just curry like just sugar or just salt. Still afraid that they might find the dish too hot, she urged them to take plenty of rice to eat along with it.

The pickles and the olives in their various forms had been prepared by Rosie, too. Since this was olive-growing country, she believed strongly that everyone ought to learn to like them.

An endless procession of small dry condiments to garnish each one's plate, moved slowly around the table. Rosie's hands were in constant motion. Her amber beads picked up the flickering light of candles she had lit in special honor of the American guests. From outdoors, the sunset was spotlighting one corner of the room where they were sitting and glinting on carved brass, copper pots and pitchers.

The American girls could not keep from gazing around at everything. How different it all was from home.

They were interested most of all in Mrs. Mookerji herself and in her sons. They were all Indians of Kenya, yet three-generation Africans. The men were wearing European suits; the mother was in Hindu dress. The maid was in a calico Mother Hubbard around which she had tied a red sash, tightly, so that her lean little figure showed. Her hair, braided in short pig-tails, was secured with small red bows which matched the sash. The food was Indian except that they had been served bottled drinks before the meal, while some of the side dishes seemed to be of African origin.

"People of whatever kind certainly have many native good qualities," Rosie was saying when the girls looked at her again. She was dipping a small ball of rice neatly into her curry with her fingers even though a silver knife and fork lay at her place. "Perhaps there won't really be peace in the world until we are all brought together in the blood that flows through our veins." She did not raise her eyes to them at all but went on with her fastidious eating. But the air was instantly electric and she knew that someone would speak soon. She already knew them well enough to guess which one it would be.

"That's intermarriage!" Jim said. He could not go that far in his thinking. Understanding and friendship, yes, with everyone, but not intermarriage.

"I shall never be an advocate of that, any more than was Chandra's and Tom's father," Rosie continued in a matter-of-fact way. "But when a mixture has already taken place, then let us not apply cruel discrimination." Her eyes did not so much as flicker as she looked about at them all, the picture of content.

"Don't you think, perhaps," she went on calmly, "that one of the great troubles in the United States and in the Union of South Africa, as well as in some other localities, is that those who have already been born of two races, are barred from their rightful place? After all, it was not exactly their fault—and I have sometimes heard it said by authorities that good and good make even better. All I am saying is: people are only people so let us not condemn them for what they had nothing to do with." Her speech finished, she turned to Boro.

"Carry the coffee pot carefully—mind you, very carefully—into the parlor and set it on the small table. Then take cups. Can you count how many? Well, soon you will be able to, now that you are in school." She spoke in English to the child, partly, it was clear, to train her further in the language.

All of them were embarrassed by what Rosie had said so simply about the mixing of blood. It could not but refer especially to the United States where a few drops of Negro blood was a basis for severe discrimination in many places. But Chandra and Tom were thinking less of this fact than of their wonder about the blood that flowed in their mother's veins. It must be some joyous, sensible kind, to make her what she was.

When they all settled in the other room for coffee, Willie's mind ran on the subject of the different peoples of America. He could remember his parents talking about the way the Government had sent all Japanese-Americans who lived on the West Coast to relocation centers during the Second World War, for fear that they might be disloyal. They suspected sabotage or something of that kind. His parents had felt as though they had been slapped in the face. His own uncle had later fought with the United States forces in that war and had been killed in action. It was hard to believe now that such a great displacement of people had ever taken place.

But while Willie's mind was wandering, Chandra's mother had begun to talk about one of her favorite subjects, Uganda, which lay straight west, and north of Lake Victoria which formed its southern boundary.

Willie looked forward to seeing something of this country when the group went to the conference at Makerere College in Kampala. He had heard that Uganda was one of the richest places in the African continent, that among the Bantu people were tribes which were some of the most intelligent, progressive, and democratic people of all. He had a mental picture of beautiful landscapes, whizzing bicycles, and lively, brightly-dressed crowds.

"I'm delighted that you are going to Uganda," Rosie could not keep from saying, looking around at them all before she concentrated on pouring coffee. "The Baganda live there and they are a merry, intelligent and, yes, great nation." She broke off, suddenly.

Chandra was astounded at her words. Surely she had never been to Uganda, yet she was speaking in this way. He wanted very much to ask her to explain why.

Instead, he turned to the others and said with a touch of aggressiveness, that as one got acquainted with the people of Africa, one would probably find many good qualities in them, even though they would still, of course, be Africans. After all, he had listened all evening, and had said nothing until now. But he had the impression that his mother's eyes had darted a look of protest at him, while he was speaking.

A quick glance went from one to another of the

Americans. They were puzzled. Why had they been invited here when Peter was among them? Jim could not leave without some kind of an answer to the question. When, after a time, they said their good-bys, he added, "You've given us *all* a wonderful welcome, Mrs. Mookerji."

"Because you are Americans, it was a great pleasure to have you," Chandra answered promptly for her, bowing courteously over their extended hands as he gripped them warmly. His mother only smiled and waved as they went away.

Americans were queer specimens, to be treated in a special way, the young people were thinking as they went quickly toward their bus stop.

"I'll bet they never invite a black African to their house," Jim could not keep from saying.

"Of course not," Willie's voice said in the darkness. "You should read your history better."

But Jim, striding along, thought to himself that while Willie might be right about Chandra, he was pretty sure that both he and Willie were wrong as far as Chandra's mother was concerned.

CHAPTER 3

WHILE Willie Miamoto had been something like an encyclopedia at Chandra's house, he had really held back a good deal of information that he had stored away. Perhaps because of the way the Japanese-Americans had been treated during the War, he had grown up with a great curiosity about the Orient. His schoolmates said that he took it for granted that the East was going to take world leadership away from the West; that though he behaved like an American, his blood was still Japanese. This made him stop and think but did not convince him that what they charged was true. The white man's invasion of nonwhite countries, even though some of them had been so rich and old, always astonished him. Why had it happened?

There had been civilizations that rose and passed before those of India and China came to their highest points. He had read of Egypt, Assyria, Babylonia, Persia, Greece, Rome and the Mayas. But their day

British Information Services, New York
The Conical Tower in the Zimbabwe Ruins, Southern Rhodesia.

had been in past ages before the time of Jesus.

There was more and more proof of ancient, highly developed civilizations in Africa of which there were scarcely any enduring remains because there were so few imperishable materials there. Yet rock paintings by Bushmen in South Africa were thousands of years old. Tanganyika in East Africa had striking paintings which were probably not as old. Nigeria must also have at one time been the center of great cultures; the Benin bronzes were called the world's best. Northern Nigeria had written records dating back a thousand years. The Zimbabwe ruins in Southern Rhodesia still puzzled archaeologists. Remnants of great buildings and abandoned gold mines made some believe that an advanced culture had once existed here. The Baluba tribe of the Congo, with a history of about three hundred years, had sculptors with a feeling for strange and special kinds of beauty.

It seemed to Willie that Christianity and trade had gone out from Europe in conquest of the world. The old and magnificent cultures of Mexico, of India and China had given way to white invaders. Yet he was sure that no nation could live under the rule of another forever.

But he still had not found an answer for his question about the white man. Why had the Portuguese, the Spanish, the British, the Dutch, the Americans and the French been able to exert such strong authority over oriental nations? The story of what they had done read like a tale of giants.

There had been a great deal to invite invaders. As an American he could easily see what the refinements of India and China would have meant to a western world that was at that time still uncivilized by comparison. The valley of the Indus River had held a splendid culture three thousand years before the beginning of the Christian era, and then something, no one knew what, had wiped it all out. Beautiful ruins, still unexplained, remained. But when the Portuguese and the British had arrived at the beginning of the sixteenth century, India's beautiful things, her spices, the fine goods of her civilization were what made them covet her trade.

India had even had a great literature in Sanskrit, the earliest European-Indic language; she had magnificent buildings, paintings, tapestries, and sculpture. But she also had disagreement among her various peoples. This made her weak before any strongly organized invader.

When the Portuguese went on to China, they met a more stubborn people. The Chinese did not have a strong government though they had for centuries honored their Emperor, the Son of Heaven. They were united, rather, because they were a strongly organized society. It was not split by racial differences or by religious conflict as was the case in India. The Chinese were proud and self-assured, feeling it natural for them to look down on every white-skinned person as a barbarian. Islam was not able to get firm roots in China as it had in India. What there was of it had been softened by the Chinese belief that what mattered was the way one behaved rather than what one's theoretical religion might be.

Bad behavior on the part of the Portuguese, who arrived first, was so much worse than anything the Chinese had imagined possible that they would not let them stay. When the Portuguese, unable to settle near Canton, took Malacca in Malaya, they sent a representative to Peking. He failed to set up any better relations between his country and China.

Later, Matteo Ricci, because of his real scholarship and his genuine love for the learning of the Chinese, was accepted and honored at the Peking court. He studied the Classics many years before he was recognized for his ability in the Chinese language and respected for his personality.

Soon after this first acknowledged contact between Europe and China, during the time when Manchus ruled in Peking, Korea was made a colony of China. In the fourteenth century, Korea had joined China under the Ming rulers to oppose Mongol invaders. Following this close contact, Korea had enjoyed a period of great cultural development. But in the sixteenth century the Japanese military dictator, Hideyoshi, invaded Korea and brought an end to the period. From then on Korea closed herself to every outside power except China. Europeans who happened to be shipwrecked on the coast and who tried to get into the mainland were held prisoner.

Korea's first contact with Christianity came through a Chinese Jesuit from Peking who began to preach

United Nations soldiers in Korean rice fields,
among Korean hills, 1950.

the new religion. He did so against a culture which was by then rich and old, Chinese in origin and yet thoroughly Korean.

Willie Miamoto's own people, the Japanese, had been the slowest to become civilized, judged by western standards. Their first great teacher had been China, though her influence had come by way of Korea, and through channels of Buddhism. No cultural influence had been as strong as that of Buddhism. As time passed, Japan had made it her own. The plans for her first capital buildings and such traditions as the tea ceremony and flower arrangement, as well as the *tokonoma* or alcove in a home, all came from Buddhist ideas. Her written language—because it was necessary to read the Buddhist scriptures—was based on that of China.

Of course the Japanese had had their own national religion, Shinto, which was rooted in man's relationship to Nature. But these rites more and more mingled with Buddhist rites. One seemed to work with the other. Shinto sense of natural beauty was often displayed in a Buddhist alcove, for example.

Willie thought that it was interesting to see how influences from within and from without had come together to make the pattern of Japanese life. This had begun to happen long before modern times.

When Europeans reached Japan, again the Portuguese came first. They arrived in 1542, introduced the musket and happily set up trade relations. The musket pleased the Japanese and changed their ideas of warfare. Now they had to have castles which would not be destroyed by gunpowder arms. This development affected architecture and also inspired types of decorations suitable for the interior of great halls.

When Francis Xavier, the Spanish Jesuit missionary, arrived and began to preach, he was well received. Some of the feudal lords even helped his cause by ordering their serfs to be baptized. Willie had read some histories which said that one explanation of this was the fact that the feudal lords wanted to encourage the interesting foreign trade brought by the Portuguese. However, trouble between the Christians and Buddhists broke out. Many Japanese Christians were extremely brave while, in spite of the danger, national leaders and thousands of ordinary people became converts to the new religion.

Hideyoshi, the military dictator of this period, became suspicious that this business of making Christians was only a way of invading Japan. He ordered all western missionaries and traders to leave Japan. By 1600, the Tokugawa Period, doors were closed to all outside contacts. This resulted in opportunity for the Japanese to perfect their own culture, undisturbed.

Willie remembered his father's speaking about the drama, the poetry, the painted scrolls—especially the magnificent screens, the wood block prints of the Japan of that day. After some of the prints had accidentally arrived in Europe as paper wrappings for porcelains in shipment, they became the rage there. What had been rather amusing pictures of everyday life, produced in large numbers through a simple printing process, grew into one of Japan's most famous art forms. France, England and then America had gone wild over the lively and beautiful prints. They became collectors' items.

Whenever Willie thought about that time, names like Moronobu, Utamaro, and then Hokusai and Hiroshige came to mind. He was proud that some of the finest Japanese woodcut originals were hanging in the world's great galleries.

It was certainly not surprising that Westerners had wanted to explore the Far East and to set up a trade which they thought would be profitable all around.

Perhaps the difficulty of finding such cultural beauty in Africa, except in Egypt, might explain why that continent had been so late in attracting Europeans. Though Egypt's culture was six thousand years old, it seemed to belong to another world. Leaving out Egypt, Africa had recorded no history of herself before the Portuguese arrived in the fourteenth and fifteenth centuries, with the exception of thousand-year-old records in a section of Nigeria. Written languages were not developed until modern times.

What had attracted the Western traders had been products which Africa could offer. Perhaps the people living there had not even known that what they had could be so valuable. They did know that slaves were valuable for these had been a commodity bought and sold by their own traders long before the white men arrived. Rubber and sugar were there, too, as well as palm oil and many important minerals of which one was uranium.

In whatever way Willie Miamoto looked at the past of the world around him—at India, China, Japan and Korea, at Africa—all the countries that were now racing to become modern, he thought of them as just behaving like people. They wanted to be recognized, to have power, to seem superior to others. Dreams of national power had lain under the whole colonial system until the world had been netted with such ambitions.

How strange to think of the British city, Hong Kong, hugging the coast of the great continent of China! How odd that Britain should ever have ruled India! Why should Africa have been chopped into sections by outside nations? Yet all this had happened because of ordinary human feelings. American and British and French ships had sailed up and down the Yangtze River into the heart of China, just as though the country belonged to them; had fired on Chinese cities here and there to protect their nationals. They had even had their foreign concessions which, for a time, at least, had seemed to be their property. Of course that sort of thing could not go on forever.

But what was always hardest to understand was how the America which was Willie's America had ever become involved in any form of colonialism. There were those who insisted that she had not—that she had not "taken" lands by military force in order to plant her flag there.

Perhaps it depended on the words used, but what about the spots across the seas where the American flag flew on islands which came into American hands from those of other foreign powers? What about the history leading up to what the geographies called "Non-Contiguous Territories of the United States"? True, history could not keep up with the present, but history was often hard to justify.

More troubling still, if one wanted to prove the United States free of all colonialism, were the occupations of modern times. They were connected with wars. Of course Japan took first place in his mind when he came to this question. It was the beginning of a long story which he had argued with Jim Smith on the way to Nairobi, and he knew they had not finished arguing it.

One thing that he noticed here in Kenya was that there seemed to be no Japanese around. As far as he could remember from what he had read, Japan had extended beyond her natural borders for three main reasons. The first was for learning, the second was for living space, the third was for trade. Learning had made her reach toward China and then Europe. Living space and trade she had tried to find, chiefly, in areas near her. If he was right in this thinking, Africa had so far not provided suitable answers to any of these three Japanese needs.

Were his classmates right when they said that he took it for granted that the people of Asia would one day lead the world beause his blood was still Oriental?

51

He had come near denying it one night on the first leg of their journey when he and Peter had been standing together at the stern of the old student ship on which they had crossed the Atlantic. They were watching the foam of the wake, lit dimly by the ship's lights and by the faint moonlight. It gave them a sense of direction and movement to stand there.

"You know," Peter had begun, "I sometimes wonder why countries develop so differently. Whenever we mention Japan, we instantly picture people who are busy, who make beautiful things, who keep their homes neat, and who are always smiling and polite. One might explain this, perhaps, by saying that they did not have much land to start with and so they had had to make the best of it. But is that all?" He hesitated and then went on.

"In the case of African countries which I have read about, and in southern communities of America where I have lived, things are not at all as they are in Japan. Life moves slowly. If work gets done on time, fine, but if it doesn't, why it's all right, too. Why? It isn't a difference in blood, we know, because your blood and mine are the same under the microscope."

"Food and climate certainly exert some influence. History, too, plays an important part," Willie answered. He traced the story of slavery in Africa, both under its own traders and under white ones. Such treatment could not avoid having an effect on those who suffered under it.

The contrast of what had taken place in Japan was

sharp to both of them, as they carried on the study. Instead of existing in a pattern of slavery which had become set, stifling all ambition, the Japanese people had been basically free. First, glimpses of China, later, visions of European culture had stung them into action. They were not going to be outdone. But they knew that they would not be able to match what they had seen unless they worked with every ounce of energy and initiative they had, for Nature had given them only limited resources. They had set to work. Though the world at first had marveled only at the delicately beautiful objects which they produced, using bamboo, woods, paper and silk, and at their fine arts, they were suddenly a world power to be taken into account.

"You are always telling me that I take it for granted that the people of Asia are the future leaders of the world," he remembered he had said to Peter that night at the ship's stern. "If they aren't, then it's going to be the people of Africa. They are getting the same view of what is outside that mine got several centuries ago."

"Freedom appeals to everyone," Peter had answered so quietly that Willie had scarcely been able to hear him. Then, as if to himself, he had continued. "No one can ever have a corner on freedom. It is like potato yeast in bread dough. You can knead it down again and again, but it will rise and spread so far that you can't believe it was so small to start with." He had laughed suddenly in the darkness and turned to

Willie. "That's a parable based on experience. Once I had to watch some bread my mother had set. I thought we would be buried before she returned."

The warm rumble of his chuckle had been comforting as they had stood there on the ship in the middle of the dark ocean. They were setting out together to meet other people from all over the world in a foreign country. Both of them were non-Caucasian and non-white; both knew what discrimination meant.

The memory of that night came back to the Japanese-American boy more than once while he tramped the streets of Nairobi and saw the strong feelings that existed between different groups there.

CHAPTER 4

O NE section of the international conference held a meeting for orientation in Nairobi, on its way to Makerere College. That evening, the visitors from America were standing on the edge of the group which had gathered in one end of a long hall.

A dark student with fine features was addressing them. He had a grievance. It was that the colonial governments seemed to discourage rather than encourage education of the native people.

"The more educated we get, the more likely we are to complain and to want to change things," he insisted. "So what happens is," he continued, "that Kenyans don't even get a chance. If they do succeed somehow in getting a schooling, who is there for them to associate with? Not whites, not Indians, and there are few of themselves." He threw his hands out in a gesture of futility and went to his seat on the platform.

Alice Svenson looked around curiously at the group

of which they were to be a part for the two weeks that lay ahead. The people making it up were all so different, but terribly interesting and exciting.

A fair-haired young fellow took the rostrum next and announced that trade and money were the foundations of the colonial system. Any Oriental would describe how early trade, then the Industrial Revolution, and even the world wars had been closely related to world economy, he said.

"He'd better put the French Revolution first, if he's going into history," Jim Smith whispered to Willie who was beside him. "Its ideal was like acid eating at the heart. No one could get rid of it, once it had touched him." It was still the hope of the world and maybe its ruin. Once subject people accepted it, it set to work on them from within, he thought to himself.

Cecilia who had overheard the whispered conversation thought acid a horrible simile. She would rather picture freedom as a vision or a beckoning light. Yet freedom had caused a great deal of bloodshed and would probably cause much more. But that was only because people were willing to fight to get it, she argued to herself, triumphantly.

The meeting went on. The Americans felt a part of it and yet far away. Chandra, whom they had brought with them, intending to please him, was uncomfortable. He wondered whether he should have come. He would never have been included except as a guest of the others.

He had recognized the first speaker at once. He was a young man who received volumes of mail. He was always standing around the post office reading it and hailing people as they came and went. It gave the impression that he had many friends in the city. He was very dark and Chandra had always been carefully polite with him but no more than that. Now here he had had to listen to him make a speech! Happily his father, Sudar, was not seeing him.

The next man on the rostrum—he almost leaped to it—was positively blue-black. Cecilia was fascinated by his dramatic beauty. There was something of the artist in her and she could scarcely keep from thinking what fun it would be to capture him in broad, swift strokes of her brush. The picture would be full of action and contrasts. As she watched, his words and gestures confirmed her impression of him.

He described the situation in South Africa as being so bad that people in Kenya could not even imagine it. As he spoke, he flung out his long, graceful hands, and took a pose. "My people have one who is called their king and a nominal tribal unity, but they are truly without freedom," he declared. His accent, and really the accent of all the people of Africa whom Cecilia had heard speaking English, was a delightful, elegant, clipped British.

"Who is he?" she demanded of Chandra.

"I think that he must be a Zulu from South Africa," Chandra answered quickly, pushing down a quick feeling of scorn. He had heard that the Zulus had been dramatized by the white man so that they had the idea that they were the magnificent African type. He knew that they used to be great warriors and cattle

57

raiders. They were still herders, but watching this man he was convinced that they liked to show off. Yet he was ashamed of his prejudice.

Cecilia remembered that the Zulus lived down at the very tip of Africa, in the province of Natal. She had located their most important city, Durban, and found that there—as it was in the case of Nairobi—Europeans, Asians and Africans formed distinct groups.

Willie listened to Cecilia's question and Chandra's answer with some surprise. He was about to add some details which might make their conclusions less downright. Instead, he raised his hand to indicate that they had all better pay close attention now.

A girl from the Belgian Congo had taken the reading stand. She was slender and wore a native dress of vivid yellows, decorated with bold designs. It suggested an Indian sari and yet was so tucked up and pleated in the back that it flared out in a highly modish manner. Her short-sleeved under blouse was of solid orange as were her slippers and stole.

"She's like a jungle bird," Jim said softly. "I never saw anyone like her."

Complete silence had fallen over the rather disorganized crowd. Every eye was fastened on the young woman. She gave the impression of being cute, bright, and yet in deadly earnest.

"Friends from many parts of the world," she began, "as one of the central committee for our youth conference which will shortly convene in Kampala, I have the responsibility to address you." She hesitated to

58

look at some notes in her hand. The way she placed her accents was delightful to the Americans.

"I am to welcome you who have come this far before we go on from here. And so I greet you who have traveled all the way from America, from Great Britain, from France, Germany, Switzerland—"

She pointed out that all of them had come here especially to study those countries which were in the process of becoming independent or those which had already achieved their freedom. The delegates would want to discuss what steps they had taken and what yet lay ahead; to consider problems of their young people and ways in which they could be helpful to their countries.

The speaker smiled on the audience with lively charm, and concluded, "We live in such a dangerous world—though we want peace. How can we who are just growing up help to bring it about? This is the underlying reason why so many of us are coming so far to attend a conference at Makerere College." She moved to her seat with the grace of a magnified butterfly, while her words hung in the air in a silence that no one felt like breaking.

The meeting of welcome ended. The young people gathered in their national units and began moving slowly away.

As they left the building, Chandra felt uneasy about the whole evening. Though it was true that Gandhi had become a world figure because of his interest in peace through the method of nonresistance, Chandra always felt out of place whenever peace was being talked about. It was not that he did not revere Gandhi. It was rather that he was more at ease in the workaday world where one did not worry about these great questions. Now he was eager to snap back into that atmosphere.

He thought very fast, came to a conclusion, and said quickly, "My brother, Tom, has said several times that it would be a shame if you left the city and did not get out to see a game park. Of course there are many important things on your minds, but he is right about this."

A look went from one to another. They had all hoped to see some parks while they were in Africa. The one closest to Nairobi had not been listed as often as others like the Kruger in South Africa, or the Albert in the Congo, but they all knew of the wonderful country of Kenya and its wild life.

Chandra felt sure that he could borrow a car. He was planning quickly while he waited for their answer. He would have the day off, since it was Saturday. His mother would pack some food and probably go with them. She always loved a picnic; was passionately fond of animals.

They stood debating what they ought to do, in the light of the entrance to the hall. No one tarried in Nairobi streets after dark.

"We'll accept the invitation," two or three said, at last, almost in unison.

The car that collected them the next day was what the Americans called a station wagon though the others said it was a carryall or a lorry. From the efficient way people and lunch were stowed, it was clear that picnicking was popular around Nairobi.

As Chandra had guessed, Rosie sat, as if at the center of the expedition, though, really, only in the center of the back seat, smiling and more than ever dramatic in a soft-toned Indian dress. The Americans did not understand that she had intentionally avoided wearing bright colors because they might enrage the animals, she thought.

"Now then, I suggest that we scatter ourselves a bit," she announced with the voice of authority which was natural to her. "Any two that go around together, sit next someone else." She waved her hands about indicating seats, tucking in her skirts so as to make more space, and generally directing the loading. How she thought anyone could be separated from anyone else in this car was so amusing that Willie was grinning from ear to ear.

When all five of the Americans and the three of Chandra's family were in, the car, though full, would have been comfortable except for the presence of the lunch basket. It certainly seemed unnecessary for such a short ride, and yet no one would have been the first to suggest that it be left behind. So it was pushed in on top of the toes of those in the middle seat and nothing was said about it. A large thermos bottle lay on Rosie's lap like a baby.

"We could almost walk there," Tom complained. "Such a great fuss to come to the park!" He was beginning to grow tall and his bony knees almost touched his chin as he sat where he was.

61

"Don't say anything; just wait. You will see the reason for all things," his mother said firmly. "Now, Chauffeur," she announced to Chandra, "we are ready."

"I'd rather go to the jungle and see the cobras and the crocodiles," Tom continued in a way that made the girls' flesh creep.

"Hush! Just be glad we do not live in such a part of Africa," his mother said, severely.

Out here, away from the town, Peter could not keep his eyes from the sky. He had read about African skies, especially over some parts of the continent. Now he knew what was meant. The clouds were billowing up everywhere, radiant with color as he did not remember ever seeing them at home. They seemed alive—skipping and racing along.

Perhaps the beautiful effect was caused by the great mountain peaks—Mt. Kenya to the north and Mt. Kilimanjaro to the south in Tanganyika. Or perhaps it was the lakes—Lake Victoria on the eastern boundary of Kenya, and other smaller ones, down through the Great Rift. He could not explain the sky, but he was so fascinated by it that he could scarcely pay attention to conversations going on around him.

Did people who always live here get so they could not *see* their skies, their great expanses of open land, the hugging, cringing acacia trees, the dry tundra grass, the glistening, hard-baked soil, the space? He asked himself this question again and again as they drove.

He could not answer it for the people of Africa even though their blood flowed in his veins. He suddenly

62

Sunset on Lake Victoria, at Mwanza.

The East African Office, London

remembered today how once his mother had said, "Son, no blood of white people is mixed with that of our people in your veins. You may be sorry or you may be glad before you get done living, but your mother and your father are right proud it's so."

He was African and he was American. Today, looking on the magnificent land, he was glad that it was in some strange far way still his heritage.

They came to a stop and all sat silent, watching and listening. Soon a group of rhythmic lines came together to form a vision of zebras. They paused, looked around, relaxed and began to nibble the tough grass. As if at a hidden signal they trotted away in graceful formation, after a few minutes had passed. Cecilia clapped her hands soundlessly in delight, her eyes shining. Jim, sitting next to her, looked down and whispered, "Right loud in their tastes, aren't they?"

"Ssh, look over there, in the reeds or whatever they are—" Tom saw her first and was pointing with a finger held low.

The female lion was swinging along, every muscle in perfect time, approaching them with the confidence of a parlor cat who was about to jump into its favorite chair. A few feet from them it came to a standstill, gazed at them thoughtfully, then dropped to a sinuous lounging position, as if it had made up its mind not to hurry. But its eye never left them, though other smaller animals began to appear, now that they were sure that the queen of them all was not hungry. Overhead, the birds seemed to be having a carnival of some kind, whirling and fluttering and crying out at each other in a kaleidoscope of brilliance.

In the short time that they could spend in the park that afternoon, between twenty and thirty of the forty different animals which lived there must have come into view—a bat-eared fox, a civet, a caracal, antelope, giraffes, buffalo as well as all the others. It was like living a fairy tale, like leaping off into another world, one so beautiful and strange, so barren and bright that it could have little to do with tree-shaded streets of America's home towns or the cemented sidewalks of her great cities.

The people in the car were almost altogether silent, for it was not possible to talk much except when they were driving slowly along. Even Rosie was quiet, pensive, looking thoughtfully at one person and then another, as well as at the animals beyond the closed car windows.

But at a certain moment she seemed to come to life and with her usual spirit took command of the situation. She said something quickly to Chandra in another language. He glanced at his watch and nodded. The car took off in a new direction and leaving the park went out toward the northwest.

"What's happening?" Tom demanded, squirming around as much as space would allow to look at his mother. She only smiled back at him, and then he guessed, "Oh, to the Rift! Good thing! Good idea!" Now he was eager as he had not been about the park which was too familiar to him.

The drive they undertook was one of thirty or so miles. When they reached their destination, they left the car and went to gaze into the depths of the Great Rift which dropped before them. The bottom of the enormous split in the earth's crust was 1,500 feet down, about thirty or forty miles across, while on its floor what seemed to be volcano craters were scattered about in a careless pattern.

"Four thousand miles long, stretching from the River Jordan in Israel, through the Red Sea into Ethiopia, down through Kenya to Mozambique and so to the sea again," Willie filled in, in his encyclopedic fashion. Rosie said simply, "Correct."

"Then a second Rift goes from Lake Rudolf to Lake Nyasa, west of this main Rift," Willie continued in the humorous monotony of a reference library.

A ripple of laughter started but was checked by sudden silence. Everyone was affected by the display of Nature around them—the gash in the earth's surface, the brilliant sky above, the sense of space, of color, of tremendous action which had at some time, no one knew how many thousands of years ago, brought this about. Yet, perhaps one day even the Rift Valley would be put to man's use.

One thing grew clearer and clearer each day the young Americans were in this beautiful country. It was that human beings would have to learn to use it so that it became part of the modern world all wanted to belong to. The people of Africa had to be people of the new day from here on. All that had happened to them up to now could be taken as history. It might

Kenya boy, once a Mau Mau follower, shows prize-winning
cabbage grown in rehabilitation camp.

serve to teach them, but at the same time it ought now to be forgotten. They stood at a turning point in the story of mankind.

"We must go," Chandra said, reluctantly, at last. "It will be getting dark by the time we get home. We still have our lunch to eat. Shall we go to the Hills for it, Mother?" He was pleased at the way plans had worked out. What a good thing he had thought of it!

Rosie merely nodded and gathered her skirts to start toward the car. She had forgotten how moving the sight of the Rift could be to those who had not seen it before.

They reached one of the hilltops near Nairobi where they could spread their lunch. Rosie began pulling it from all sorts of interesting packages in the basket. Vivid sunset was making the sky even more magnificent. The heat of the afternoon was giving way to the chill of evening.

"Look about you," she cried. "Is not our land the most beautiful in all the world!" She was passing out breads and bean paste, spiced meats, peppery pickles and sweets while she went on. "From what I had heard said until today, only America, only England had the real beauty, while Africa was all jungles and snakes and sleeping sickness and horrors. Now you have seen what it is and you will never forget . . . There are, too, the beautiful animals." She sighed, then her black eyes danced again as she looked over her guests. They were all eating with huge appetite.

"So much of Africa will be changed when industrialization comes in," Alice murmured. "Factories and everything will spoil lots of places."

"But it matters more about the people than about the country," Cecilia argued. She was thinking about the gathering in the hall where the Kenyan had spoken first, about the Zulu, about the Congolese girl from Makerere College who had come to welcome them. They were splendid just the way they were; they might be spoiled if they tried to act like Westerners.

Her eyes fell on Chandra as he ate. His delicate fingers parted the sections of a bun, laid cold meat and pickles inside, closed it before he took the first bite—all with the most elegant gracefulness. He was Indian rather than African, in the truest sense of the word. She remembered watching a black man eating at a little wayside place they had passed in their way. A leaf was his plate, his fingers, his silver, and yet he had consumed his food neatly and efficiently. How ridiculous that everyone should have to wear the same kinds of hot, uncomfortable clothes, make a ceremony of eating food, and set up a lot of other pretending. Yet, she had to smile, because she could just hear some of her friends protesting, "But, Cecilia, there are no people in the world who like to pretend as much as the French!"

Well, perhaps Africa was changing her. She looked out over the wide expanse and across at the town. She loved it all.

"I guess we have to keep remembering that it's the Africans themselves who want to become modern nations, now," Jim said carrying on her thoughts.

"Things have come to a point where they would be the last to say, 'Leave us alone. We'll stay as we are.' But *something* will be lost forever."

Willie did not feel like getting into a discussion, but he had definite opinions about what lay ahead for industrializing countries. He was certain that the need for money would bring great changes. Every modern economy was based on finance. To compete in a modern world, a country simply had to produce and get into the world market. Japan had become a major power because of her industrialization. Russia and China were following the same course. Each country of Europe had gone through the same process, led by England and then by America.

"Nothing important is ever lost," Rosie said, picking up the conversation where Jim had left it, so seriously that the others looked at her in surprise. "None of the outside things that happen to a people really matter. The inside ones do—such things as what they think of themselves."

She said no more but began to collect the lunch that was left. They all helped her, thinking of what she had said. They were puzzled by her, too, for she was both old and young, ancient and modern. She was Indian and yet not Indian. They liked her immensely.

70

CHAPTER 5

THE day after the young Americans left Nairobi the town seemed empty to Chandra, and even to Tom. Though Tom was younger than the others, he had become their satellite. He had not often joined in the conversations, but he had listened and thought over what was said. He had never been so interested in other nations, freedom and big subjects like that, before in his life.

Chandra had been surprised, often disturbed, but still delighted with the visit of the young people. They had talked so urgently about democracy—even for the dark-skinned. But then, they had not lived in Africa. There were lots of things they did not really know about.

These young people from outside—mostly from outside, anyway—had acted as though *they* had to see to how other nations were acting, or criticize their own. He found it hard to be in sympathy with such a point of view. Planning and authority had to rest somewhere. He took many things for granted. It had been proper for him to prepare himself to be a post office clerk and it was right for him to expect certain salary increases as time moved on. He had never dreamed of going to a university because none of his friends had done so. They were business men, tradesmen, clerical workers. If one began to confuse social groupings, no one would know where he belonged, and everything would be most uncomfortable.

But he had discovered that the Americans thought anyone ought to have the right to go as far as he liked in education or in position. In fact the word "right" seemed to be a favorite one. What was more astounding was that everyone who was connected with this conference group, no matter what part of the world he had come from, was talking this way. The only exceptions he could think of were those from countries where the government was very strong and the people did not have enough courage to speak out.

My, but he would never forget that girl from the Belgian Congo who had stood there welcoming them in her delightful costume. She had implied that they, the young people, were going to be able to find solutions to the world's difficulties, a way to peace and economic security. Again someone had been talking freedom—and a woman at that!

What was this! He studied a letter carefully. It bore a Nigerian stamp and was addressed to a section of the city which he knew was largely British. The return

British Information Services, New York
Pollination of palm flowers for selective breeding, Nigeria.

address was a school of some kind and a small mistake in the way one letter was written had caught his eye. It was from a student, that was it. Perhaps if he worked here long enough he would become a real sleuth. He put the letter in its proper box and went on with his work.

The summer was well along now. He had better settle down and put his mind on his job. He must help Tom with his school work more than he had been doing. He ought to take more responsibility at home—and he felt a good deal of pride in this thought. His mother would be growing older and he was the first son. It was the tradition of his people that he should become the head of the house.

Watching Tom grow up made him wonder if he had been the same at Tom's age. He had often heard it said that no two children of the same family were alike. Surely he and Tom were not. He had always been a rather careful boy, planning things out and then doing them. He remembered that he had taken great care of his clothing and of his few imported toys and books. Tom tended to be quite careless and to throw his things about. He liked to make exaggerated statements. Now that he was changing from a skinny small boy into a tall fellow who liked to eat, the contrast between them was even greater. Tom was jolly and loved a good joke. Often one he thought of as good did not seem funny at all to his brother.

When the conference in Kampala was ended, the American group was to fly to London from Uganda's second capital, Entebbe. He, Chandra Mookerji, had better just put his mind on his work and his responsibilites and think no more about those who had dashed in and out of his life.

But he found this hard to do. Not only he but also Tom, his mother, and some of their acquaintances were forever recalling something the young people had said or done. This was because they had had such a questioning, demanding attitude toward everything. They were like voyagers seeking a new Utopia of freedom and justice.

Thinking eastward to India, China, Japan, the Philippines and the lands of the South Pacific, and westward to America, Chandra wondered whether Africa and even his own people here, could still be half asleep. Perhaps if he had lived in India he would have been more like the Americans. Had he always lived there, probably his family would have witnessed, perhaps even have taken part in, the great things that had occurred in India. They would have felt that the granting of independence to the Philippines, for instance, was much more significant than he thought they had here. It had come so shortly before India's own freedom from Great Britain—and if any country knew the meaning of a struggle to achieve this, his did.

He was only a small boy when Philippine independence was declared on July 4, 1946, but he still remembered his father reading the paper that told of it.

"July 4th," he had murmured. Then in some hidden

corner of his work table he had found a small, crumpled American flag, attached to a pin. This he had fastened on Chandra, smiling and saying, "Well, then, one western country has kept its word to an eastern nation—and that country is the United States of America. This day we shall fly its flag, if only by means of small Chandra."

The child, seeing his father, whom he adored, smile, had pressed the flag hard into place so that it would not loosen and fall and had rushed into his mother's out-stretched arms. "Freedom," she had said in a strange way, her eyes on something far off as he did not like them to be because he wanted them there, on him, on them, on their room. "One day every country in the whole world will have it—whether its people are black, or brown, or yellow, or white." Her eyes had come to his father then, and both had smiled in a secret sort of way.

But that was all years ago now and they were so long exiles in Africa that they seemed scarcely to belong to India.

Not until years later, in school, had he learned something of the story of the Philippine Islands. He had found that they had been discovered for the West by Magellan, and taken by Spain in the last half of the sixteenth century. Manila, already a busy town, grew into a center for trade, not only among the islands and nearby China, Japan and Borneo, but also for trade with Mexico, which was then under Spanish control, with Siam and India.

The Spanish had imposed Christianity while they were trading. Having only one religion helped to break down many old religious and tribal divisions. It unified the people who were of Negrito, Malayan and Indonesian backgrounds. Arabs had been there before the Spanish came. As Moslems they had made only another division among peoples of the islands. Nor would they become Christians.

Gradually, Filipinos who became successful in business under the Spanish government grew into a powerful, wealthy class. They were content to leave things as they were among the less fortunate, since they themselves were quite comfortable. The poor people, workers on plantations and laborers of all kinds, lived very hard lives. They had no hope of improving conditions unless they could find someone who would champion their cause.

Spain had dominated the islands for three hundred years by the time that such a champion appeared. He was José Rizal, a young student, of Chinese, Spanish and Malayan blood, who had studied in Europe. It was while he was there that he seemed to have been touched by this biting acid of freedom which Jim Smith talked about.

At first Rizal expressed himself in books of fiction. His first novel was so strongly against colonialism in the Philippines that he had to smuggle it into the country to a printer there. Once the Filipinos had the book, it became their symbol. By now the situation was tense and dangerous. Thousands who had dared to express revolutionary ideas were in exile. But as they heard of Rizal and his book, they became electrified with the thought of fighting for their freedom. In the Philippines, the Spanish tried their best to ban the book. They arrested those they suspected of hiding it. Houses were searched. Such measures only increased the feeling against them.

When, in 1887, José Rizal went home to find out what the situation was, he saw at once that he must not stay if he hoped for anything to come out of his efforts. He left by way of Japan, went to the United States and then on to Belgium. There he had a second book published. This he dedicated to three Filipino priests who had been badly mistreated for their loyalty to the ideal of freedom. It stirred Filipinos even more than the first book had done.

Rizal returned to the islands, determined to act. He formed the Philippine League through which he hoped to organize the people and keep them under control while definite plans for progress could be made. But he was arrested by the government and exiled to the island of Mindanao for four years. There, he was helpless.

This gave the hotheads among the people a chance to push on hastily. They founded what they intended to be a secret society; it behaved in an undisciplined manner; rumors exaggerated whatever happened; the Spanish government became more and more severe.

In jail, Rizal was desperate. He had to find a way to get out, to save his country. He asked to serve as a doctor in the Spanish army which was active in Cuba at this time and his request was granted. But he was arrested again before he ever arrived there, brought home and executed.

Rizal's death had solved nothing. The Filipino revolutionaries knew that they must appear to be inactive for a time. Meantime they heard promises of change on the part of the Spanish leaders; they did not believe that they would ever be carried out.

When the U.S.S. *Maine* was blown up by a Spanish bomb in the harbor of Havana, Cuba, the Filipinos warmly sympathized with the Americans. They recalled how the colonists had fought for and won their freedom. Now they took up the cause of the United States in Cuba. When America declared war on Spain the people in the Philippines supported her heartily. Aguinaldo, the new revolutionary leader of the forces, an exile in Hong Kong, joined in the American attack on Manila Bay. That day the Spanish fleet was destroyed and the islands came under the control of the United States. Now, surely, independence had come.

But for the enthusiastic Filipino freedom-seekers it turned out to be only the beginning of another stage of foreign rule, beneficent though it was compared to that of Spain. They were deeply disappointed when they discovered that while they were helping the United States to free their country from Spain, they were delivering it into American hands.

They resisted the new invader in every way they could. This was largely by guerilla warfare since no

79

Philippine troops were left. America poured her forces in while the Filipinos fought them desperately for three years.

Whenever guerillas were captured, the authorities hoped to get some helpful information from them, for they wanted to end the fighting. Nothing could be discovered even though torture was sometimes resorted to. When word of this reached the United States, the people demanded an investigation. Just punishment followed. This swift action made the Filipinos respect the Americans, in spite of bitter disappointments.

But the big question in the United States was what to do with the islands which were on their hands. If they were left alone, it was argued that another colonial power would simply move in, for some said they were not ready to govern themselves efficiently. President McKinley believed that the United States was under obligation to keep them under her care, but that when they were prepared they should become independent.

A new American government for the Philippine Islands was established on July 4, 1901; teachers arrived from America; schools were started and the "care" of the Filipinos began. But now pictures of José Rizal hung beside those of Washington and Jefferson on school room walls. This was strong reassurance to the people.

Gradually the Filipinos began to believe the promises of the American conquerors. Steps were actually taken leading toward that moment when independence would be a reality. Meantime, the people were learning more about how to conduct a democratic government. At last a date for independence was set.

No one could have guessed that the Second World War and occupation by Japan would interrupt the twelve years between the promise and its fulfillment. When, at last, the Philippine flag replaced the American one all through the islands, Manuel Quezon, the first president of what had become the commonwealth —who was also to have been the first president of the independent islands—was dead. Manuel Roxas was elected in his place.

A Far Eastern, colonial, nonwhite country had become independent. This, Chandra realized as a young man, was what had made his father pin the little flag on him years ago.

Yet by the time of Philippine independence, events much more significant for them as Indians were already taking place in their home country.

Sometimes in the early afternoon when there was a pause in the post office, Chandra thought of the country from which his grandparents had come. He realized that Nairobi had none of its feeling, except as the Indians themselves had re-created its atmosphere in the part of it where they lived. True, much of India was hot and likely to be swept by monsoons as were parts of Africa; languages and ways of living varied; there were not enough schools.

Religions had been important in the history of his

country. They had often brought on divisions and bloodshed, though Buddhism with its philosophy of brotherhood and compassion had originated there. Too, some of the poorest people in the world lived in India, sleeping on the streets at night and always hungry.

Castes which divided society had been carefully observed until modern times.. There had been great thinkers among the Brahmins; fine artists and artisans among the middle classes. Indian culture was ancient and magnificent, known across the world. India had

Press Information Bureau, Government of India, Washington, D.C
School for adults in an Indian village,
Moradabad District (U.P.).

had a great literature before it was ever written down. Bards had narrated poetry and tales, some of which became a part of European literature in later ages. Though thousands were still unable to read, new methods of teaching were being used today.

Names like that of Asoka, the great liberal philosopher and leader, flashed to Chandra's mind when he thought, even quickly, of his heritage. He thought, too, of modern men who were still at work for the new India—men who were revered and listened to all over the world. One of these, chief of them all, was Prime Minister Nehru. But he could not think of Nehru without remembering, first, Mahatma Gandhi. That slight figure was always appearing and reappearing even in his life here in Nairobi.

Chandra could hear his father saying, "The Mahatma need not have changed his whole life, risked himself and gone to prison. His father was a prime minister; he was sent to London to study law—but no. This idea took hold of him and he could not free himself from it."

At this point Sudar would look up from his fine sewing and gaze at his son through small-lensed glasses as though expecting *him* to explain the enigma. Then he would go on. "It all started in South Africa. Gandhi went there as a lawyer to work for a law firm, found the Indians were being hatefully treated, set up a kind of center at Phoenix, near Durban, and began to plan his method of bringing about change through civil disobedience." Again Sudar would pause and gaze at his

83

son, finding it hard to explain to a child just what Gandhi's method was.

Chandra had had this brief statement about Gandhi filled in a great deal as he grew up. The small man had not always been a strong-willed leader. He had failed his first case because he was so shy that he had become confused. But when he was sent to South Africa on another case, he had asked to travel first-class on the train only to discover that 100,000 Indians were second-class citizens in that part of the world. They and the five million Africans were ruled by fewer than one million white settlers.

He was treated brutally as he crossed Natal and was able to find a place to live in Pretoria only through the help of an American Negro. After that, his determination hardened. Yet his view was that fighting to champion the cause against colonization must be done in ways that would decrease rather than increase hostility.

Gandhi had organized the Indians of South Africa in a nonviolent resistance movement during the next years. When the Boer War broke out, he interrupted that work to provide an Indian ambulance corps of eleven hundred men who sometimes carried the wounded as much as nine or ten miles to camp hospitals.

What had changed the young man into this kind of leader? Chandra remembered that one day he had asked his father this question. By now India was moving toward independence under Gandhi's leadership . . . The sun had been shining sharply into the small room which was littered with sewing. When Sudar had looked up, his thin arms were spread in the familiar gesture of stretching thread between needle and knot, though at the time it had seemed more of an outreaching motion.

"Before the day came when he stopped his movement to help the wounded of the Boer War, the Mahatma had prepared himself. He gave away all his property; he moved his family to a communal farm. He said that he no longer wanted to be a first-class citizen. Something had taken place inside him, and he saw the suffering of his people in a new way."

Sudar had broken off and resumed his sewing. He was easily moved by thoughts of Gandhi, yet he realized that he could never be like him. It was bred in him that his first duty was to his family and his group. He could not go through with such a degree of self-sacrifice, though he greatly admired it in others. Let those who were stronger than he follow Gandhi's way.

Yet as Chandra grew a little older, father and son had often come up to this question. Because it was so puzzling, Sudar each time tried to put it more clearly in words. "He believed that man's soul and will have power that can change himself and others. He made up his mind that it was wrong ever to use force to get even what was right, because force would destroy some of the good in it." Sudar usually had to stop there to bring his thoughts together before going on. "He saw his own people suffering all kinds of wrongs and he was determined to help them—but he did not believe that he would really be helping if he brought on bloodshed, or even bad feeling, in doing it. The *way* he brought change was as important to him as bringing the change, you see." Chandra only half saw then, and even now.

Whatever his personal feelings were, Gandhi's organization of Indians led to the establishment of the South African Indian Congress in 1898. In modern times this still had a membership of nearly fifty thousand people.

When Gandhi returned to India he became the leader of the movement for independence there. He searched the sacred books of Hinduism, of Buddhism, of Christianity and related their teachings to his method of nonviolence though he was not an adherent of any one religious group. When he believed that he or the thousands who came to follow him were falling short of the spirit in which independence must be won, he disciplined himself, and indirectly others, by long fasts which sometimes brought him near death. The people followed him, largely caught his intention, in time almost deified him.

On August 15, 1947, a little more than a year after Philippine independence had been proclaimed, India was free. But, in a way, it was a disappointing kind of freedom because her two great religious factions, the Hindus and the Moslems, had opposed each other so strongly that the only solution for the time being seemed to be to divide the country. India lay flanked by East and West Pakistan to her north. Having done everything he could to bring the people together in order to avoid this separation, Gandhi though first of asking his followers to protest in a great, passive movement. He decided, after long fasts which had been undertaken to bring about co-operation, to still reject the decision but to take no action against it. By its own choice the new India was to remain within the British Commonwealth.

Only a few months after India became independent, on January 30, 1948, Mahatma Gandhi was assassinated. As Gandhi was going to a prayer meeting in the garden of a friend, a demented young Brahmin pushed forward and shot him.

Chandra had always tried to take part in the memorial services which the Indians in Nairobi held each year. They chanted songs and hymns which the Indian leader had especially loved and read from Hindu books and from the Mahatma's writings. When he went, Chandra felt that he was doing it more for his father than for himself. He had been too young to feel the heavy gloom which was said to have wrapped not only India but also all the world on the winter's night when the news of Gandhi's death flashed through the air. Prime Minister Nehru had said, "The light has gone out of all our lives." Truly, Sudar had said, it was like a darkness settling over the land.

Jawaharlal Nehru had had to lead India through the shadows. Chandra was always fascinated by photographs of this man. He was so handsome, so well educated; his face was delicate, sensitive. In every way he seemed to be the opposite of the small, spiderlike Gandhi.

87

Nehru came from India's highest caste—a Brahmin of Kashmir. His father had been a lawyer, his family well off until it began to lose what it had in the independence movement. Nehru had studied in England, at Harrow and then at Cambridge.

When he returned to India as a young man, the independence movement had not yet sprung into life. In the years following the end of the First World War, Gandhi became a close family friend of the Nehrus. Nehru's father was one of the early leaders in the movement for India's freedom from British rule. The whole family was gradually involved in the nonresistance program set up by Gandhi; some served prison terms so repeatedly that the experience came to be a familiar one. Nehru himself spent several years in jail.

Follower of Gandhi though Nehru was, the two men were greatly different. Nehru was devoted to independence, believed in Gandhi's ability to lead and in the nonviolent method which he used. He did not share the religious conviction which was the secret of Gandhi's strength.

Yet when Gandhi was gone, Nehru seemed to be more affected by the small leader's principles than he had been before. History showed that he had to be the one to guide India through the difficult days when her economy had to be strengthened swiftly, when one world crisis followed another and decisions had to be practical and clear.

Chandra, the young man, was often proud that his homeland could be the mediator between nations which were at the point of war. Though Prime Minister Nehru had never claimed that he would maintain Gandhi's position or not use force if he thought it necessary, and though he did not resort to fasts to purify himself or to bring others to co-operation, he was trying in every way possible to avoid military activity.

More than that, Chandra knew from what he saw in the newspapers that India's Prime Minister was heard with great courtesy and attention whenever he spoke before bodies at the United Nations or whenever he addressed his own Congress. When he conferred with other national leaders, it was headline news.

From all Chandra could find out, India had made great progress in the ten or more years since Gandhi's death, even though it was still divided. . . . He would never forget that though Gandhi's last wish had been that his assassin should not pay for what he had done with his life, in the end the courts ruled that he must do so.

India had become free without a bloody revolution and even without real bitterness toward the colonial power which she had suffered so much to be delivered from. Sudar had once said in his slow, thoughtful way, "Britain is getting India ready for independence, I expect, teaching her how to govern herself in a modern world, and training men for her offices."

It was strange to think that a country should control another country and at the same time prepare it for its freedom. Yet some declared that the United States had done just this with the Philippine Islands, that Britain had done it with India and was doing it with some of her African colonies. Since they had no right to be there, surely it was the least they could do. When colonies became independent, at last, their preparation for it would probably be very apparent.

Sorting the letters which came each day, studying their post marks and their writing, it seemed to Chandra sometimes that even postage stamps told something about nationalities. Some of the tiny oblongs were about nature, or history, or art, but others were symbols of imperialism or of freedom. Some were miniatures of struggling people.

Lines of communication from all over the world came together and passed through the Nairobi post office. Chandra wondered whether, if he could really have felt them, they would not have been red-hot, lukewarm or cold in the intensity of their emotion.

CHAPTER 6

S TAMPS from Communist China were vig-
orous and lively, their colors brilliant and
eye-catching. Chandra had been told that they were
characteristic of the country under its new leaders.

The four-cent stamp showed throngs marching, carrying high huge banners of Mao Tse-tung with the date,
1958. This was the year by which the steel production
of China was to have been doubled. Steel mills appeared in the distant left corner of the stamp.

The eight-cent stamp had the same theme. People
were smelting their bits of metal on any kind of fire
they could concoct in their own backyards, in the
shadow of towering refining plants.

What had set the Chinese people afire with determination to progress? From all that Chandra had
learned about them through his studies and the conversation of his elders, the Chinese were solid, humorous and common-sense. They respected learning, took
life philosophically, and worked hard at whatever they

could. Yet southern Chinese were aggressive merchants all through Southeast Asia, and in scattered points far from there.

Two stamps of 1959 commemorated International Women's Day. The first one portrayed women in five callings, those of steelworker, peasant, salesgirl, student and militia woman. Attractive, yes, but also very daring and militant. The second stamp explained women's changed position in Chinese society. A Chinese and a Soviet woman stood together with their arms entwined, lifting a banner bearing the celebrated date, in the foreground. In the background Chandra could make out the dim figures of oppressed women in other countries.

These stamps set him to wondering. Did they truly represent the opinions of the Chinese people? Could this be the China that his India had always thought of as her friendly neighbor, interested, like herself, in learning and the arts? As far back as recorded history, the two nations had been like brother and sister—one practical, humorous, down to earth, dignified and holding all its people in the range of dignity—the other tending toward mystical religions, abstract thinking, less inclined to enjoy humor. Yet here was China breaking away from her own past, it seemed, and certainly no longer so closely related to India. China was ready to sacrifice everything to modern progress, it appeared.

Such a direction had started with Dr. Sun Yat-sen, the leader of the Revolution, and founder of the Republic of China. Yet when he died, his will, though not actually written by him, stated, "The Revolution is not yet accomplished." Could he have guessed how significant these words would become?

Dr. Sun had been educated in Christian mission schools, gave up the practice of medicine in order to lead the people toward a new form of government. In all pictures of him which Chandra had seen, he had looked mild, even weak, certainly not like Rizal of the Philippines, nor like Nehru—yet less gentle than Gandhi. In the end he had proven not only gentler than Gandhi but lacking in his determination and ability. He had served as an inspiration rather than as a leader.

When he died, hopes which had at first been so high and which had been supported for a time by the democratic countries of the West gradually weakened. The Chinese people were divided between loyalty to General Chiang Kai-shek, the new leader of the Nationalist Movement and a more liberal group. This group was affected by all that next-door Russia was doing in a movement toward progress, as Dr. Sun had also been. But Dr. Sun could not know so early that the Russian Soviet state and, later, this group in China would become highly organized dictatorships rather than truly Communist republics.

When Japan invaded China in 1936, the Chinese Communists joined with the Nationalists under General Chiang's leadership. They helped to defeat the Japanese, and they also pushed the Nationalist Government itself from the mainland to the island of Formosa. In Peking they established the Communist Chinese People's Republic under the direction of Mao Tse-tung.

The task the new government faced was that of

modernizing a country which was not only nonmechanized but also wasted by war. It appeared to be overpowering, but the new leaders set to work with energy —and with ruthlessness.

Chandra had meant to ask Willie more about what he thought of the Chinese Communists. Perhaps he would have had a clearer opinion than most people. One heard terrible things about them. It did seem to be true that the new leaders thought the cure for China had to be swift and drastic—that they must blaze the way for progress, as they saw it, or else fail completely.

The people had long been promised better days. Now the time had come when what they knew of conditions in the West and what they had been taught about freedom by missionaries had to revolutionize their lives. General Chiang had not been able, or perhaps even willing, to devote himself to bringing this about. The new leaders were.

China had one fourth of the people of the world; it was practically nonindustrial. What industry there was, was almost altogether in the hands of foreign interests. The new government seized large holdings of land, redistributed them, organized man power in co-operatives and in collective farms—and, when even these did not produce enough by 1958, in communes. These were made up of thousands of households or several villages. The government took women out of their homes, put them into industries set up with urgent speed or on the farms. Babies were cared for in nurseries while their mothers worked. Children were sent to school or to youth camps. Convinced that literacy

Pushing forward in the Chinese People's Republic.

was the foundation of progress in a modern age, the government started schools for all ages and simplified the written language. Dr. James Yen had pioneered in this years earlier in the Thousand Character Movement which developed a limited vocabulary and printed books within its range. But the Chinese People's Republic went further than he.

According to the most reliable authorities, the first step in this swift progress had been purges to get rid of all those who would not co-operate in it. No one outside China would ever know how many thousands had lost their lives because they would not change their minds. Millions had had to conform outwardly but still resisted inwardly.

The greatest psychological revolution, perhaps in all history, had been attempted in China since the Communists had come into control. The new government had changed the family system so that it was now the community or the national system. Parents no longer controlled children or expected respect from them, but the government most definitely did through its local offices. The young led rather than the seasoned old. Scholarship was respected only if it was the new scholarship which was rooted in propaganda upholding Communistic nationalism.

Hatred for the white man, the Westerner, was a favorite theme for a parade; hatred of Western scholarship and Western religion.

Chandra often thought over all these strange things that were taking place in China. He wished that he could find out more about them. No Chinese seemed to come to Nairobi. There was strong feeling against them because they were such clever businessmen. There would be feeling against them now because they were Communists. Yet Africans usually connected Communists with white-skinned people!

After all, shouldn't the non-Western people realize that their first urge to industrialize and to compete in the modern world had come through Western influence? While it was true that great nations had existed in the past, white men had undeniably been the ones who had spread ideals of freedom and tastes for modernization. Even Russia, which was considered white, had changed because her people wanted to be free of a cruel nobility. India, China, the Philippines and now the countries of Africa were following the lead of the white men, if in their own ways.

He was suddenly right back at Jim's way of putting it. The acid of freedom could not be gotten rid of and it ate deeper and deeper into man's thinking as time passed. It came to be the thing for which a man and a country would sacrifice anything.

Was this what had happened to China? Had not her people been touched by this acid—lightly through Dr. Sun, burningly by the early Communist group which could not then see where its devotion to Communism would take it? Later, as in every great movement, leaders had to take control, harden policies, cut off what would not fall in line. As history so often recorded, these new leaders in time became new oppressors from which once more the people might have to seek escape.

But the time had not arrived yet in China when her people would want to throw out their new leaders; probably it would not for many years. Success, freshly discovered abilities, and "a place in the sun" for what had been termed a "backward" nation by Western standards were like an elixir which made the young fearless and tireless. They could *see* their country growing modern—factories, dams, schools, better transport, greater production of food, if not better food at least more food for all, a new literacy, a new language— were all proof of it. What if one did not say certain things, did not look backward but only forward, forgot the sacrifices and remembered only the accomplishments? This was a new China and the rest of the world would have to pay attention to it.

All this was outward. Much harder to understand was what seemed to be the inward change in the Chinese people. Human nature could not be altered so quickly, Chandra thought. Not unless it had to, to survive, he added with a sinking feeling.

Wondering about what was happening in China, Chandra was suddenly glad for Mahatma Gandhi and Prime Minister Nehru. He was even, for a moment, grateful to the British Government. India was changing, modernizing, as was her neighbor, but she was doing it by easier stages. She was respected among the nations of the world, and though there were black marks against her, particularly because of her religious disunity, she had passed through no such terror as

China had. She was not in the hands of any dictatorship under whatever name. She was able to serve as a mediator. Her ancient cultural values were still important; her literature was still real. Was this, Chandra often wondered, because the Mahatma had counseled peaceful methods of change so strongly and so successfully that though Prime Minister Nehru could not go all the way with the little teacher, he and everyone was still feeling his touch? Was India's acid of freedom sweetened by his gentleness?

This satisfying thought came especially one afternoon when it was nearly time for Chandra to close up and go home. The cool air blew in the open doors, catching the corner of a golden-colored sari worn by a woman who was coming in. The light silk surged in like a visual breeze before her. Sunlight was still brilliant outdoors, outlining the buildings sharply. Chandra had been so far from his own homeland in time and distance that he did not often think of it as he had today. It must have been the sight of Chinese stamps which had set him to going over it all. Aggressive, militant, determined—was this the only way a nation could win recognition in the modern world? How could one think so when country after country of Africa was soon to step out on its own? Many of them were going to do it with almost no power to support them because the day of their freedom had arrived. It was as inevitable as birth or death—and as significant.

CHAPTER 7

H UBERTUS was small, agile and quick to smile, perhaps sixteen or seventeen years old. He and his family had managed to come to Nairobi from Indonesia at the time when it had become independent from Holland in August, 1945. Then thousands of Dutch colonists were repatriated or went elsewhere. Certainly Hubertus was not pure Dutch, for his small bones, his soft, dark eyes and his yellow skin all showed that he had Indonesian blood, too. But this had not affected the fact that his parents were colonists in every sense of the word. His father had been the owner of a large tea plantation, used to giving harsh orders to the Indonesian laborers and demanding service from a retinue of servants.

All that was in the past now. But there were very few other people of Dutch origin here in the city; life must be lonely for Hubertus and his family— Of course there were large numbers of his people in other parts of Africa like the Gold Coast or Ghana as they called it now, Angola, the Cameroons, and most of all in South Africa— But Hubertus was in Nairobi.

One day Tom spoke to Hubertus and walked along with him on the shady side of the street, though they were scarcely acquainted. A sudden impulse had taken Tom, a thing that happened rather often to him.

Embassy of Indonesia, Washington, D.C.
Harbor Construction in Indonesia.

"Suppose you've heard about the Asian Games," the Dutch boy said at once, eager to be friendly.

"No, what?" Tom demanded, for he was always interested in sports.

"I thought that that was why you decided to be so civil today," Hubertus answered, smiling in a bitter sort of way. "They're to be held at Djakarta, capital of Indonesia—of the *Republic* of Indonesia—in August, 1962. I thought everyone must have heard. Offered to have them there, they did, making a grand gesture."

"Oh, you must be sorry that—well, perhaps they would not interest you—" Poor Tom broke off realizing that he did not know what he was tumbling into with his faltering words. His first thought had been that Hubertus must be terribly sorry to miss the great event. Then, he had realized that probably now Indonesia was the least likely of all places to attract the boy.

"If you think I would wish to be there for the spectacle, quickly change your ideas," Hubertus said gruffly. "It's all a great show. I know those people and I've been in Djakarta often. It's a filthy place—has an awful canal running down the center of the city. The people are lazy and don't have the least idea what independence means. They need to be told what to do, like the niggers in America. They'll do nothing on their own except wave flags, talk about *merdeka,* independence, call each other *pak* or *mas* or *bung* all of which mean 'brother,' more or less, and then go right on doing nothing."

"The books I have at school don't make them out as

bad as all that," Tom said, greatly confused and also embarrassed. It seemed as if the Dutch boy had opened a secret door which led to a closet where he had stored unpleasant thoughts. He might one day be sorry he had opened it.

"Books always like to make things better than they are." Hubertus laughed. "I know all about them. It wasn't worth wasting time in school so my father made me a clerk in the plantation office. It was great fun to tell those fellows, and women, too, just how they were to turn out the work, for a change." His face had taken on a harsh expression while he was speaking. Watching it, Tom decided that he had better be going his own way—only, he would like to know more about the Games.

"Where in Djakarta are the Asian Games to be held?" he asked. "There'll be a lot of people going, I should think."

"That's the biggest stupidness of all," Hubertus muttered. "They're building a new stadium. It's to hold 100,000 people. Of course they've had to borrow money—$12,500,000 on credit from Russia along with some Russian experts. The Japanese—ha, old friends —are putting up $8,000,000 for a huge hotel, highest building in the country." He threw out his hands in a gesture of shock, thrust them hard into his pockets, dropped his head to his chest and walked slouchily along, eyes on the ground.

"Maybe it'll do something for the people," Tom said cheerfully, realizing a moment later that it had a childish, Pollyanna sound.

"Them! I don't know what books you've been studying, or who you've been talking to, but *I* can tell you a thing or two firsthand."

They found a spot where the shade was increasing. As he listened Tom understood gradually why Hubertus gave everything he said such a hostile slant. He had lost his home, in a sense his country, when his father could no longer stay in Java. And, too, Indonesia was the first of the Asian countries to become independent from colonialism.

Probably its earliest inhabitants had come from the rich plains of the southwest Chinese mainland. Indians, Arabs, Spanish, Portuguese and English had tried to rule parts of the coveted islands from time to time.

It was Holland that took full control—not all at once and not directly but through the United East India Company. As its power increased, it got its export products through a widespread plantation system which introduced actual serfdom. The record was bitter in the minds of those who suffered under it. On the other hand, the Dutch did not interfere with local customs, did not compete with Islam to make Christians out of the strongly Moslem people. Nor did they try to educate the people or prepare leaders through study abroad. Little was done to modernize the islands nor would this be expected when to do so would work against colonial enterprises. Yet Dutch scholars in the islands were meantime quietly discovering the riches of their cultural history and would in time give the Indonesians bases for great self-esteem.

The independence movement began in the intellectual society, Boedi Oetomo, which favored the Moslems and began to dream of a holy war against the West. However, Indian influence was strong in the Society and Tagore, the great poet and philosopher, as well as Gandhi, would not have favored any such plan.

Seeing that change was on its way, as early as 1901, Queen Wilhelmina of the Netherlands had said, "The Netherlands have a moral duty to perform toward the people of the Indies." Forty years after that, she repeated the statement. It was by then too late to bring independence by any moderate method.

The Mohammedan Party began to make demands at its Congress sessions, and the Dutch tried to satisfy it by allowing for larger Indonesian representation on the People's Council of the colonial government. Then, change was hastened by other events of history—a threatened Second World War. By the end of 1939, before Holland was attacked by Germany, the first all-Indonesian Congress was called in Batavia. Such a step meant that the demand for independence was being recognized. Invasion of Holland by German forces, a Dutch government in exile in London, made it so that the next steps had to be taken in the Far East.

When the Japanese attacked the Indies, all the people united to resist them. They hated the Dutch but they hated the Japanese even more. The Dutch authorities tried to check the entrance of Japanese into the interior but failed. In the fashion typical of invading armies, the Japanese had a holiday in Indonesia, ruining the land and the people. It was only when the Japanese themselves grew afraid that Russia was going to enter the war that they began to try to work out steps to free the Indonesians. Perhaps if they had known that the war was going to end so soon, they would have been less willing to recognize this wish for independence.

The Indonesians had tasted the flavor of freedom and nothing would do in its place. Dr. Achmed Soekarno took the lead, though a younger and more scholarly man, Soetan Shjarir, understood the principle of revolution better than he. Shjarir knew that the present movement really had nothing to do with the Japanese invasion. It was the same ground swell among human beings which had brought on the American War of Independence and the French Revolution. In 1946 he wrote in *The Voice of Free Indonesia,** "We absolutely deny that our movement springs from rancor. Without hatred, without resentment, but as keen as ever, and with no less passion, do we stand in this struggle for principles and values that in the long run determine the sense of human life."

By gradual steps the independence declared in 1945 took shape. A constitution, which had been begun earlier, was completed and put into action. A People's Bank was established, new industries were begun, universities were opened. As had been the case in India, steps of separation from the colonial power were gradual. The first stage brought about the self-governing dominion of the United States of Indonesia within the Dutch empire. Complete separation and independence followed.

---

*Quoted by Robert Payne, in *The Revolt of Asia,* John Day, 1947, p. 59.

Yet here in Nairobi Hubertus was speaking against Indonesia as he was. Tom wanted to know more.

"Tell me what the people of Indonesia are really like," he asked.

"Them? They don't care, that's the real trouble. They get all excited when a leader speaks to them, and by the next day they're thinking about something else. They just like to tell stories and sing songs and dance— take it easy, you know, and not worry about anything much." He smiled easily, himself, and at that moment he seemed more Indonesian than Dutch to Tom.

"They're not taking it easy about the stadium," Tom protested. "You said yourself that they were working hard to get it ready."

"That'll be a big show for them to put on." Hubertus shuffled uneasily. "Just the way in the revolution, some of them did fight bravely—but then, probably the Japanese or the Communists put them up to it or made them."

"Still, that's saying that they *can* work hard and carry a thing through, if something or someone puts them up to it," Tom insisted. "Perhaps they want to do really well in the Games and as host or do well as a Far Eastern country that hasn't been independent very long." Tom could feel his face getting red while he was speaking. Why was *he* standing here taking up for a people on the other side of the world anyway? Could it be that the respect that the Indonesian leaders had had for India was affecting him even over here in Kenya?

There was another reason. It was that he believed

that a longing for freedom belonged to everyone and that the longing had to be satisfied in the end. Where had he gotten that notion? From many places, he knew, even though he had never stopped to think about it like this before.

Well, he had spent a long time here. Now he turned toward the Dutch boy and raised his hand in signal that he was leaving. Hubertus only shrugged his shoulders, grinned, and said nothing.

A week after the Indonesian Republic was declared, Vietnam in Indochina had taken the same step. Burma had followed soon after.

Indonesia had been largely Moslem; Japan, Buddhist. Burma was chiefly Buddhist like Japan. This religious unity could have been used as a basis for Japanese authority in Burma, and perhaps it did play a part in an early, desperate effort on the part of the Burmese to win independence from Britain and from India. For thirty Burmese belonging to the Dobamma group, made up largely of university students, eager for freedom, had gone to Tokyo. There they had made an agreement with the Japanese to found a national army of liberation. They were anxious about the spread of the Second World War at that time and felt that something must be done quickly to protect their growing independence. In return for loans to set up this army, Japan asked only for special trade privileges and for control of the Burma Road. This road was then highly important as the only land route between China and India. It was not clear then that, had the Allied forces not been victorious, Burma would have been a colony of Japan. When the Japanese did invade Burma in the course of the war, this army of liberation which they had helped to set up in Burma was a convenient tool for them. These 30,000 men really, innocently, brought about the fall of their country. It amounted to an invading power being invited in.

British Information Services, New York
Burmese peasants in the rice fields.

Still, the Japanese had misjudged personality. They had not realized that the Burmese are one of the most dignified people of the world and that they would not suffer indignities. Of ancient Mongol origin, coming down through China, they are gentle and refined. When the Japanese soldiers rampaged and wrecked the countryside and mistreated peasants, the seeds of a thorough revolt against the new colonial power were sown. Burma would throw off Japan just as certainly as she would throw off England and India.

A young man belonging to the Dobamma group again took the lead in the revolt. Aung San said that he admired Nehru more than any other leader. He believed that the basic problem of colonialism was that foreign countries came and invested large sums of money in their colonies in order to produce goods for export rather than to help the local people. He was a socialist and felt that socialism was practical in the Far East because of the low standard of living and because of Oriental religious philosophies.

Burma's authority was put into military hands in 1958 in order to insure uninterrupted progress without foreign interference. One reason why Communist China did not interfere seemed to be its wish to avoid entanglement with India over Burma.

The story of rising independence swept on through the years until by 1957 Ceylon, as well as Cambodia and Laos, bordering Vietnam, had joined the newly free states. Farther south, Malaya was having a harder time because her people were so varied and so divided.

110

British Information Services, New York

Left to the old and right to the new in Singapore.

The Malays hated and feared astute Chinese business-men, some of whom were loyal to the Nationalist Government on Formosa, some to the Chinese People's Republic. Indians in Malaya were largely plantation workers who felt they supported the Indian Congress at home. Malays themselves were support-ing their own leaders or the British crown. When the Second World War broke out and when the Japanese invaded, secret feelings came out and some Malays welcomed the invaders because they hoped for better times under the Japanese.

Singapore brought together more different peoples than perhaps any other geographical point in the world. Here, at least, no one group seemed to be above another.

Independence was coming slowly in Malaya. But, at last, in 1957 the Federation of Malaya became a self-governing member of the British Commonwealth. In 1958 the island of Singapore also became inde-pendent, although a British High Commissioner was still responsible for defense and for cultural affairs. Because they were afraid of Communist influences, the people of the peninsula were anxious not to give up the support of non-Communist powers. This may have been one reason why it seemed wise not to throw off British connections entirely, too hastily.

France's only large and important possession in Asia was long known as Indochina even though this was made up of a number of smaller states with differ-ent histories and cultures. They were Annam, Cochin

The King of Siam's summer house in Lake Bang-Pa-In,
supposed to have been built in the memory of the
queen of King Chulalongkorn.

China, Laos, Tonkin and Cambodia. About seventy-five per cent of the people were Annamites who are of Chinese origin and usually Buddhist. The Cambodians and Laotians show strong Indian influence in both religion and language.

In modern times Annam, Tonkin and Cochin China are unified in Vietnam, although that unity has again been broken since Vietnam's northern part turned Communist while the southern part remained French controlled. The relationship between northern Vietnam and the Chinese People's Republic was much like that between the latter and North Korea. The countries of Indochina seemed to be leaning more and more toward Communism, bringing France's power in Asia near its end.

France had set up a protectorate over Cambodia far back in 1863 and soon forced the next-door Siamese (Thais) to give up all territory east of the Mekong River which runs down the peninsula. This was the origin of Indochina, but it became only part of a larger contest between France and England over the countries of Southeast Asia.

Siam had lain between the moves of the two great powers. By clever maneuvering she was able to keep free from them partly because of her location. Both agreed to Siam's independence in an Anglo-French treaty of 1896.

Siam, or Thailand, again saved herself from being put under a joint protectorate of France and England in 1917, by declaring war on Germany. During the

Second World War she co-operated with Japan because she so hated European imperialism.

As time passed and waves of nationalism swept over her, it grew clear that in order to modernize her government and her army, Thailand must have men with Western education. Students were sent abroad to study. But they were largely chosen from aristocratic families and when they returned they tended to be conservative. This fact worked well, from one point of view, for reigning King Rama VI was an Oxford man. He founded the Chulalongkorn University and set about creating a modern literature; he established Western sports, began youth organizations and tried to interest his subjects in their responsibilities as citizens. A strong Buddhist, he started a revival of Buddhism.

In spite of changes brought by moderate and reasonable methods, revolution broke out in Thailand in 1931. It opposed royal autocracy and appointments being given to members of the royal household. It was determined to free the economy from foreign control.

Chandra often glanced at a map on the wall of the mail room to make sure of his geography. It was not up to date and he knew that the colors used had once shown the relationship of certain areas to colonial powers. He thought it over as he worked. In every case the cause of empire had been economic. There was no other good reason why countries should reach halfway around the world to grasp land and workers. This was what Willie had declared, too.

Spices of the Orient had set off the search for exotic lands at a time when spices were preservatives as well as seasonings. From then on men had reached eastward by long overland caravan routes. They had explored eastward, too, by sailing westward across uncharted seas. The New World as well as the fabulous Orient had been discovered for the Old World as a result. And trade had been the magic word. With trade had gone Christian missions, and then in time it grew clear that both enterprises would be more secure when political ambition found reasons to protect them. Chandra smiled to himself remembering how his father had pointed this out.

Because white men dominated the colonial expansion, it was natural that their culture and especially their languages should be transplanted to many different soils. But no one guessed that the hardiest single item that was transplanted was the ideal of democracy. Nor could anyone foresee that a time would come when the Oriental or the African would sacrifice everything for the dream which the colonial empires had unknowingly given him.

For traders and missionaries were actually laying a groundwork for revolution. Freedom, equality, and economic security were to become as precious to Filipino, Indian, Chinese, Burmese, Indonesian or Indochinese as to the American or the Frenchman.

Language played a strange and dramatic part in colonialism because there had to be a tongue in which to carry on business between foreign trader and local

Getting ready for independence in 1946; British Council
librarian and a bookmobile in the Gold Coast
(now Ghana).

merchant. This was especially urgent when no common language already existed in a colony. That provided by the traders had a broader range of communication than had any other, and, more invitingly, it formed new connections with other parts of the world. Both within such a country, and without, the imported language of business affected communication.

So it proved that English became the most-used foreign language in India, Burma, Ceylon, Malaya and then in China. In usage it became almost a slang language which was most often known as "pidgin" English, or business English.

When Japan began to industrialize, it was largely through her contact with Germany. German became Japan's business language, but soon English was in greater demand because it was more widely used.

In Europe, French had long been the language of culture. A girl in England, in Elizabethan times, was simply not educated unless she could read French literature, converse fairly well in French, and perhaps compose a few poems or write letters in that language. The same ideas about culture were carried to the New World wherever French influence was strong. In the southern states where English influence dominated, French held the same importance.

Dutch, or some form of it, was used throughout Indonesia. French was the business language as well as the language of culture in Indochina. Thailand probably mixed more languages, foreign and other, than any other Far Eastern country.

The fact that languages from across the world could become so important, first in the Far East and later, in Africa, told the shameful story of the white man's aggressiveness. For where in the West would one find Chinese the main language of business and scholarship? Where would one find Hindi, or any language of India in demand—and this even though ancient Sanskrit of India and most European languages share the same roots? Where would one find Swahili from Africa in common use in the western hemisphere?

To succeed as teachers, doctors, businessmen, or to become scholars, young people of the Far East or of Africa knew with some resentment that they had to learn a language of the West, best of all, English. For beginning with the building of the British Empire, English became a world-wide language.

Introducing foreign languages into a country brought some unexpected results. They could be learned only in special schools, not in national ones because there were not enough teachers who knew the foreign languages. Only a limited number of students could be taken care of in the private schools both because of their scarcity and because of the fees. This meant that the starting of efficient national systems was sometimes delayed.

What was perhaps even more important was the fact that modern science studies were available only in European languages, chiefly English and German. As science was more and more eagerly wanted, pressure for learning foreign languages increased. Though as time passed scientific textbooks would certainly be-

119

come available in many languages, the pressure to know English continued strong. The only way to get into a university in the home country was to have a command of English; study abroad depended on study of an advanced kind in one's own land. English was the stepping stone to all well-paid jobs in the colonial system and in the professions. Young nationals begged to be taught English.

To know this foreign language was important in another less obvious way. Knowing it was the only means of finding out what people of the Western world were thinking about. Teachers of English and the teachers who taught their subjects in English were the ones who could express those ideas which were most alive and most important in a changing world, it seemed to the modern Oriental student. He wanted to know those ideas, for he, too, wanted freedom, had ambition, and was ready to step into the new day.

After the first revolutionary steps had been taken, after republics or new monarchies were declared, the fact to be faced was that reorganized governments had to have trained leaders. They ought to be ones who could understand the present times, who had a grasp of industrialization and of the techniques of organization.

Under this pressure, the values of the past were for a time pushed aside. Riches of ancient cultures seemed antiquated. Philosophies which would become the only real hope of a world threatened by nuclear disaster were buried temporarily under the rush toward modernization.

CHAPTER 8

ONE morning Chandra noticed again an envelope with the wrongly written letter in the return address.

The summer when the American group had come was long over and Christmas, 1959, was near. Sunshine was blistering hot in the streets because of the latitude, and people were doing only the most necessary errands, walking along borders of shade wherever they could. Ideas of snow, associated with this Christian holiday, belonged to some other part of the world. Just the same, mails were heavier than normal and this letter with its identifying error carried a Christmas seal in addition to its Nigerian stamp.

It was hard for Chandra not to imagine what the writer was like. He was probably a small, careful, hard-working student who was asking favors from some kind person and who, because of wanting to be correct, made unusual mistakes. Large glasses, bent shoulders, threadbare clothing came to mind. True, the Christmas seal was not quite in keeping with this kind of image, but then often seals were given away by teachers in Christian schools, or, for that matter, they might be used over and over with a little care and some fresh glue. He studied this one a bit and saw that, indeed, it had been put on with something besides its own stickiness. This made him feel foolishly triumphant.

He was certainly not prepared to recognize Mr. Okoli, the writer, when he entered the post office one spring morning weeks later just as the rainy season was beginning. The tall, broad-shouldered smiling man, glistening with moisture, had the bearing of a person who expected everyone in the world to be his friend. Not that he had any special reasons to expect favors, but simply because he believed people were that way.

He strode toward the mail window where Chandra stood, perhaps because their eyes had met instantly, and said a cheerful "Good morning," with such enthusiasm that the young Indian could only gasp a quick reply. The man was extremely black and his manner unusual for Africans in Kenya.

"I shall be getting some mail here," he said now, "and I thought perhaps it would be well for me to leave my name here with you. Is that the way you do it here?" His eyes glistened and his teeth were dazzling when he smiled again.

"Sign here," Chandra said shortly. "I shall watch out for whatever comes and you may call for it at the hours posted beside the main door."

Mr. Okoli signed his name, giving his home address. It was then that Chandra could not keep from noticing the odd, identifying letter which before had marked the letters from Nigeria. It was impossible not to say something about it.

"You have sent a good many letters here," he remarked in an offhand way. "You may wonder how I have happened to notice yours among others. This is why." He pointed to the wrongly written letter and was conscious of feeling great satisfaction as he did so.

"No, really, I don't wonder at that at all," Mr. Okoli laughed again. "I expect that others have thought this little symbol of our brotherhood, foolish, too. You see there is a small group of us who are aspiring to scholarships abroad, and, as a sign of our unity in this hope, we have turned this letter around when we exchange any letters on the subject. We knew that whenever that symbol appeared, however inconspicuously, we would have a kinship with that person, even though we had not even yet met him."

He explained it simply but it had wide implications. Chandra was taken aback, not so much at finding that the error was intended, as that this dark-skinned man should be so unbelievably ambitious and determined to move to higher positions in the world. But, he remembered suddenly, many Nigerians had gone to London to study before this. Why should there be such emphasis on it now? Why should a Nigerian be coming eastward across Africa?

Overlooking the question of handwriting, he said with some condescension, "I should have thought that you Nigerians had long had scholarship opportunities in England."

"Ah, yes. It is so. But there are other parts of the world with great civilizations; there are many who want scholarships. Some are of darker skins than others—" He broke off.

British Information Services, New York
Teen-age girls at the Katsina School, Kaduna, Nigeria.

"Then you are not planning to go to London?" Chandra was becoming curious about this fellow in spite of himself. "I hope to go to India—your great country," Mr. Okoli announced. "Students from Africa are being offered scholarships there. Perhaps I—we—shall win some."

Chandra said nothing for he was stirred and confused. What was going on among the Africans? From all sides the same rising movement could be felt. Now came a man from Nigeria, a lord of a fellow, striding in the door, smiling on all the world, explaining about his brotherhood of those who were after scholarships! Even to India! It was one thing for the Americans to mix up all sorts of people and to have their own peculiar ways of behaving; quite another for an African in Africa to be quite so unconscious of his proper position in society. Chandra was altogether uncertain what his attitude toward this man should be and he definitely believed that he would have to have a firm one.

Today he did not carry the conversation any further. Mr. Okoli moved away in the crowd. But he was by no means lost in it for he conveyed an atmosphere of noticeable good cheer with him as he looked down on those around him.

During the next few days the Nigerian did not reappear and Chandra was relieved. However, he found himself thinking about West Africa a good deal. It was different from East Africa, he knew. But all of Africa was changing so much.

He knew that many countries made up West Africa and that several colonial powers had long ruled it. Then gradually at first, and now swiftly, independence was coming to them.

French West Africa was historically a huge territory running from Algeria in the north, to the Atlantic Ocean where it curved under the bulge of the continent, on the south. It met the western boundaries of Libya and the Sudan which, as well as Egypt, were for a long time under British control.

British West Africa, a kind of bite out of French territory, had included Nigeria, the Gold Coast or Ghana, Sierra Leone and Gambia. This area was long known as the Slave Coast because of its trade.

West Africa listed also Liberia, the free home of repatriated American slaves, Ivory Coast, the Cameroons and Guinea. These all had different colonial affiliations through the years. Now in 1959 one could truly say that all the countries of West Africa were either independent or in different stages of progress toward independence. Algeria, Uganda, Tanganyika and Kenya might soon be the only unsolved problems except for countries lying to the south.

The land formation of West Africa was unlike that of East Africa. The great Sahara Desert stretched across it. It was part of the enormous plateau which formed so much of the continent and which rose sharply from sea level. This sudden rise made rivers rush along in plunging waterfalls, spoiling their use for navigation, and giving the coast few bays and inlets. Thousands of square miles of grassy steppes, barren lands with scarcely any rain, were enclosed by a narrow strip of green on the north which was watered by winter rains, and by the beginning of a lush jungle zone on the south. The jungle zone extending from about 15 degrees latitude north of the equator to 20 degrees south of it had two wet seasons. South Africa had a rainy period in winter. While Lake Chad marked the edge of the moist area, there was nothing anywhere in Africa to match the string of magnificent lakes that ran down through East Africa in the Great Rift Valley. These gave the world some of its most scenic falls . . . But on the east, too, the mainland was tilted up in such a fashion that its tableland rose high above only a narrow border of lowland which fringed the sea. The continent as a mass was unwelcoming, with almost no good harbors, high internal barriers and sandbars which choked streams and rivers when they came to the ocean.

Why was it that people who had not been in Africa long enough to know better always thought of her as a land of jungles and terrific heat? It could certainly be hot, and there were jungles in certain parts, but the whole northern stretch from east to west was high tableland, gashed only by the Valley of the Nile leading down to the Great Rift Valley. Grassland, scattered low acacias, bright-colored soils, then eastward, hills and sky-piercing peaks were more characteristic of it.

Better information would have made it easier for

Chandra to understand Mr. Okoli's attitude, for in Nigeria almost no color bar existed. What had made the difference? Was it the people themselves or the way they had been treated by the British Government? Although the country was more than ninety per cent illiterate, its officials were often Africans. Yet slavery had dominated the history of Nigeria for three hundred years. Although the British had outlawed the slave trade in 1807, it continued for more than fifty years after that because it was so profitable. A bad form of liquor traffic had followed, which used the poorest grade of product and sold, to the Nigerians, at the highest possible profit.

Lagos, meaning lagoon, the capital, was a city which mixed modernism and tribalism. It had fine buildings and horrible slums. For in Nigeria three strong forces were at work. The first was a hasty move to modernize; the second was an effort to unify opposing sections of the country; the third was a surge toward nationalism.

Nigeria was to become independent in 1960. It would be better prepared than many other newly free nations. A man like Mr. Okoli could go in search of scholarships, holding his head high.

Just west of his country lay the Gold Coast, now called Ghana, separated only by the narrow strip which was Togoland. It had been the first colony of "Black Africa" to get its independence, from Britain, in 1957. Here, once more, a people seemed to have reached the point of independence from a colonial

First bridge across the Volta River in Ghana; one of the
largest of this type in the world.

power without feelings against it. Ghana was further along, proportionately, in providing education for its children than any other African country.

The Ghanaians were an interesting, unique people. They liked to dress in the style of their leading tribe, the Ashanti, who wore togas like the Romans of history. This was, also, the tribe with which the slave dealers had carried on their business along this coast, a warlike and dominant group.

Government House, the political center at Accra, the capital, was an old fort, built of Danish stone which was brought across the sea in ships as ballast. It stood on a promontory bought by Danish slave traders from African chiefs. Control of the fort passed back and forth between the Danes and Portuguese traders until the British made it into an asylum for the insane at the time they took over the Gold Coast. An isolated, wildly beautiful spot, constantly pounded by the sea, it became Government House in 1900.

In modern times Accra was not a trim city, but it was a lively one. It combined ancient history with the ultra modern in its togalike dress and the fantastic prints worn by its twentieth century women. There were smart-looking, uniformed policewomen—and handicrafts which were still carried on in age-old ways. The city was aggressive, funny, modern, old-fashioned —and took itself very seriously. Though business was thriving, thousands of people were extremely poor.

Who could know Africa? She was everything. Nothing could be said that would include all her many

Mothers at school in Ghana.

sides. Her own people could not have a broad view of her because they had not traveled far enough. Those who visited often went home to talk about Africa or write books about her, not realizing that they should speak only of the one microscopic spot that had come into their view.

Some could live in Africa for a long time and yet not see the broad sweep of her lands and peoples because they had given themselves to one place or one undertaking.

Such a one was Dr. Albert Schweitzer, whose name was known across the world. He lived in French Equatorial Africa and had a hospital at Lambaréné, Gabon. The people loved him and their sick flocked to his care. He did not try to make them follow Western ideas of sanitation and perfection and seemed to understand how they thought.

Chandra Mookerji had been much puzzled by what he had heard of Dr. Schweitzer. It seemed that this great doctor would put his hand to any kind of work, for he had no sense of superiority. He revered all life as the Buddhists did and would not kill or hurt any creature. He had given up his profession as a promising musician to become a doctor because he wanted to serve humanity. Visitors from distant places who went to see him often came away feeling that he was one of the truly great. Again, some found him a strange, headstrong man with whom it was hard to work. Others enjoyed him as a brilliant conversationalist, accomplished musician, and author. Still others complained of his standards of hospital service. But none could miss the power of his religious devotion.

Dr. Schweitzer was over on the other side of Africa from Kenya. The great doctor had not traveled to lands lying to the north, east and south for he had truly buried himself in his work.

White men who had pushed their way into this continent had had their various reasons for doing it. These were more than those of the trader and the missionary. Africa had invited the adventurer more than, perhaps, any other part of the world. To outsiders it was mysterious, with few and forbidding entrances—a land of giant apes and pigmy men; of ivory and gold; of peculiar animals and odd vegetation; of even stranger people. It had the reputation of being impenetrable. This was in itself a challenge to the venturesome spirit. It was this that had appealed to Mungo Park, the Scottish explorer who had traced the Niger River to its source. It was this that had appealed to James Bruce, the first white man to find where the Blue Nile joined the White Nile. It was also this that had appealed to David Livingstone and to Henry Stanley who, whether to make Christians or to explore, were fascinated by the mysterious secrets of the Dark Continent and its peoples.

That many peoples lived here, that many nations occupied the varied landscape did not become common knowledge for a long time. Bushmen, Bantu and Sudanese, Hamites and Semites, all made up the inhabitants of Africa. When colonial powers took this part and that for themselves, their divisions paid no attention to tribal lines. Some tribes lay partly under one power, partly under another. The colonial political groupings were like one network superimposed upon another. To the Africans, the real boundaries were the tribal ones.

But in spite of the white man's slowness in understanding the black, pressures for independence had grown. Tribes or nations which wanted to be recognized in a modern world discovered that they had to accept the patterns of western culture. Where preparation for it was carefully made, the change from ancient to modern took place unexpectedly well. Where there was too little preparation, bloodshed and confusion followed.

CHAPTER 9

C HRISTMAS, 1959, passed and the new year began. At least sixteen African countries were scheduled to become independent in 1960. Nonwhite countries would actually outnumber white ones at the United Nations when this came about. No one could guess how smoothly the changes would be made.

Because of riots a year earlier, Belgium had promised the Belgian Congo independence in 1960. In June 1960, Premier Lumumba proclaimed the Congo Republic. The Belgians withdrew after an absolute control of seventy-five years. Confusion and antiwhite riots came in a deluge. The tremendous territory had not been well enough prepared for freedom.

While the Congolese girl who had been a delegate to the conference in Uganda was well educated and ready and able to be a leader, she was an exception among her people. Behind her lay 13 millions composed of Bantu, pigmy, Hamite and European origins.

Most of the 116,000 white people were Belgians whose homes and work were there.

The Belgians had done a great deal for the six main sections of the colony—Equator, Eastern, Leopoldville, Kasai, Kivu and Katanga. They had helped to build engineering projects, had established schools and hospitals, and had opened lines of transportation. The opportunities for development were tremendous. The Congo was a country of rich, low plateaus stretching above unmeasured mineral resources. Half-covered by forests, it was drained by the mighty Congo River, which offered almost unlimited possibilities of hydroelectric power.

But what the Belgians had accomplished in this promising land was too little compared with the needs of the people.

The government was so centralized that some declared that the highest form of state capitalism known in history had come about here, for the colonial government controlled all business. Feelings of discontent which had arisen among the Congolese from time to time had been tempered by the offer of jobs, by improving social services, and by keeping the standard of living rather high. But the people did not have many civil rights. Though color discrimination did not appear openly, a "separate but equal" system was in force. Job levels were closely related to color. One did not find Congolese engineers, architects or attorneys, for example. Positions which promised increase in salary after a period of service were usually available only to Belgians.

There was no close contact between the home country and the colony. Scholarships to Belgian universities were rare and only recently had a branch university, Lovanium, affiliated with the University of Louvain, been established in the Congo. Belgian

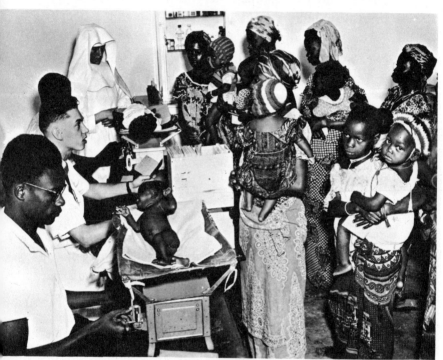

Belgian Government Information Center, New York
Lovanium University, near Leopoldville, Belgian Congo, holds its maternity clinic.

leaders in the colony had been heard to remark that it was to the advantage of the Congolese not to have their independence until they were ready for it. One wondered if they were being made ready.

When the unprepared Congolese government collapsed and disorganization followed, the United Nations tried in every way it could to help stop bloodshed between fighting political factions, and to bring order. No one could predict the outcome nor how great the suffering on the part of many people would be.

What happened in the Belgian Congo was terrifying and sad, but a longer and even more complicated struggle for freedom had been going on in South Africa. This struggle had a curious aspect. For the people who were demanding their own way were not "native" Africans but Afrikaners. These are the descendants of Dutch farmers who came in by way of Table Bay on the Cape. They arrived some time after the Dutch East India Company planted its first permanent post there in 1652. By now they had lived there so long that they had established their own way of life and their own economy. They did not even seem to take seriously the possibility that Africans might one day want their lands. Though the Bantu, the predominant group, had pillaged Afrikaner farms from time to time in protest, the white men still did not seem to hestitate to claim them. Nor did it seem unreasonable to them that 2,000,000 Afrikaners should govern 14,000,000 Africans.

The opinions of the Dutchmen were so fixed that

news of rising independence in other parts of the continent either seemed to have nothing to do with them, or they simply added it to other problems that they had had for a long time. The division between racial groups, which the Dutch Afrikaners held firm, seemed to belong to an earlier period of history.

The British had brought the authority of the Dutch East India Company to an end in 1795, at the time of the French Revolution, had occupied the Cape and then bought it in 1814 when Napoleon was coming to the close of his power. British settlers, traders and missionaries had poured in and displaced the Dutch farmers who would not accept the new ideas of the English newcomers. Another era of colonial domination by white men in South Africa had begun.

Spreading out over the veld northward, and so coming to south-central Africa, the Afrikaners had come face to face with the Bantu with whom they competed for the territory. They fought it out with one group of them, the Zulus. The day of that victory is still a great Afrikaner holiday.

After a time the Afrikaners established two small republics in their new location, the Orange Free State and the Transvaal. Britain agreed to their independence in the Rand River Convention of 1852.

When gold and diamonds were discovered in the Transvaal in the 1860's, the Bantu were further exploited when floods of European and British adventurers poured in.

The two small Afrikaner states were, meantime,

not carrying on their governments in a way which pleased the British to the south. England finally intervened and tried to take over the Transvaal herself. This led to the Boer War.

President Paul Kruger of the Transvaal expected that Germany would help him. The Orange Free State did join the Transvaal. Many people sympathized with the Afrikaners, or Boers, for they thought that they were fighting for freedom. Led by De Wet, Smuts and other able men, the Boers were able to fight on for a long time even though they were poorly armed compared with the British. They had the advantage of a familiarity with the terrain and a knowledge of guerilla warfare.

The Treaty of Pretoria made the Orange Free State and the Transvaal British colonies in 1902. In 1909 these countries became equal members in the Union of South Africa along with Cape Colony and Natal. Concentration camps for Boers made homeless during the fighting became one of history's recorded horrors, for crowding and poor sanitation brought infant mortality as high as fifty per cent, while disease and death among adults were rampant.

Once the war was over, the British Government tried to show a conciliatory attitude and to win the Afrikaners to a more liberal point of view on questions of race and government policy. They hoped for co-operation and friendliness under the commonwealth arrangement. Field Marshal Smuts, a man admired all over the world, was outstanding for his willingness to work it out in this way. Though many shared his view for a long time, it grew dimmer again, and the old, tightly knit Afrikaner group which would take no steps toward realistic modernization, took the lead once more. In the year 1960 many things would still remain to be solved in the Union of South Africa. Riots, racial outbreaks and suppressions continued. But the Union was an independent nation, ruled by no colonial power. In this it was unique, though it was hard to know what was really happening there.

Yet in spite of all the problems of the past and present, the map of Africa had changed a great deal, even since 1956. The move toward independence had increased in power when Ghana was granted self-rule in 1957. There had been republican forms of government in some countries before this, but they had been carried on under the oversight of the United Nations or of some particular nations.

By November, 1960, the spaces on the map which would still indicate by their color that they were dependencies would be the Spanish Sahara (Rio de Oro), Algeria, Angola, Southwest Africa, the Federation of the Rhodesias and Nayasaland, Mozambique and East Africa. Great Britain was trying to find solutions for her relationship to the Rhodesias and East Africa, especially Kenya. Tanganyika was under United Nations trusteeship, though still a British colony. President de Gaulle spoke of establishing Algerian independence.

Faces of newly freed people were in the pages of

newspapers and magazines all over the world. Chandra saw them in the mails in Nairobi. He could not miss feeling the surge of independence that was sweeping from country to country. Nomads and tribesmen, women and girls, students and teachers, miners and factory workers, policemen and soldiers, political leaders and their opponents—were all there, but with a new air about them, a new dignity. Chandra was

Voting in the presidential elections, Dahomey, formerly
French West Africa, December, 1960.

reminded of the Americans. *They* had had that look. And the girl from the Congo, and the Zulu . . .

"But I am an Indian," he told himself one day. "Whatever has taken place in India is only part of my family background. Whatever is going on in this continent is not really my affair. It need not have anything to do with me. What would happen in Nairobi if the Africans began to think that they could live where the Indians live; if the Indians moved to where the Europeans have their homes and businesses? What if Africans refused longer to do their proper work but demanded to be teachers and clerks? Life would be all mixed up and there would be no certainty about anything. I might be displaced by an African who happened to be clever. Then none of my plans would come out right!"

He would not permit himself to go further in this uncomfortable way of thinking. Things just had to continue as they were in Nairobi. Let other countries dance about in their new ways and upset the order of life, but this must not, could not, happen in Kenya.

Reaching this point in his self-reassurance one day, Chandra looked up to see Mr. Okoli standing before him, smiling. Chandra did wish that he had not come this day. All that he had been saying to himself suddenly lost its power and he found himself exclaiming to himself mentally, "*That's* how much what you have been thinking amounts to! Kenya might change, too!" No, would change, he already knew.

"Good day," Mr. Okoli said with great good cheer.

"I've come for my mail, again." He glanced over his shoulder to see whether anyone was behind him and then leaned easily on the window sill when he saw there was not.

When Chandra brought the few letters that had come, he hoped that the great fellow would take himself off at once, for he was not in the mood to listen to him, much less talk with him. Besides it was getting near the hour when work was at its heaviest. A line was beginning to form behind Mr. Okoli.

The oppressive heat of the beating sun glimmered up from the floor, and the light from the pavement of Delamere Avenue was almost blinding, though the shades were partly drawn. Chandra wanted no questions asked of him either outwardly or inwardly. Let things be just as they were.

The Nigerian seemed to see something of Chandra's mood, for he took his letters, glanced carefully at their return addresses, and turned as if to let the line fill his place. But as an afterthought, he paused to stoop and look in the window at the Indian.

"I thought you might like to know that I shall be going to New Delhi," he said. "Plans are working out. I shall be studying co-operatives and village organization." His smile became brilliant. "I shall be seeing you again when I come for mail at least once more. It occurs to me that perhaps you might have a message for me to take to some person there—or a suggestion of someone whom it would be helpful for me to look up." He could not know how long ago Chandra's people had come to Africa.

Nigerian weaver at work on traditional patterns.

Chandra tried to think quickly what to answer, but the Nigerian, afraid that he was already making the line behind him impatient, turned and left at once. Good thing! What a stupid question!

A message to India? Why should *he* have a message to anyone in India! Almost three generations had passed since his ancestors were there.

He handed the letters out automatically, answered questions, tore sheets of stamps apart, accepted money —but underneath it all another question was rising to the surface of his mind. He could not quite phrase it yet, but the words for it were coming.

"If I am still acting like an Indian here, why have I no message for India when someone I know is going there? Am I African or Indian? If African, why am I behaving like an Indian, if Indian why have I now no message to send my homeland?"

He finished the rest of the afternoon's work with a kind of numbness in all he did. Everything in his plans had always been sharp and clear until now. Now his thinking was troubled and confused. He had asked himself a question—but did he have to answer it?

CHAPTER 10

S O OFTEN when Chandra was thinking deeply about something, or when Tom was full of what seemed to his brother to be ridiculous ideas, their mother suggested a plan or an excursion which cleared the air. As he grew older, Chandra thought of her as being too simple, too childlike, though often very comfortable. But Tom was not yet old enough to see his mother as just a person. She was still the one who said "yes" or "no" to his requests—yet she was also great fun, *if* annoyingly stodgy.

Tom towered over Rosie now, for in the last months he had stretched up to a great height. Watching him on the athletic field, Chandra was really astonished at his large, well-built frame and at his natural grace and agility. On the other hand he could not keep from being a bit sensitive that *he* himself was so slight. But, he reassured himself, he was like his parents and, besides, he had no wish to be an athlete.

Chandra's moodiness following Mr. Okoli's friendly

offer to carry a message to India for him was lifted by Rosie's suggestion that they have a small family outing. They had cousins in the city whom they almost never saw. Once in a while Rosie's conscience bothered her because she was not more hospitable to them.

"We are quite horrible in the way we forget Kumar and Krishna," she said after she had suggested the plan. "I do not know why it is that they do not seem to fit in with us, naturally. I am sure that is why, without really meaning to, I put off having them over. I should be ashamed." She was looking pensively out the window as she spoke, into the small back garden which she had carefully developed through the years when she knew that they would probably never move to another house. "But now I feel the need of seeing mountains, anyway," she added.

No one knew how much the sight of mountains meant to Rosie Mookerji. No one but her husband could have guessed.

"Well, it's quite all right with me to invite them over to picnic on the Hills," Chandra answered his mother. "Kumar tries to be too modern, almost 'beatnik' as they are calling it now, and Krishna likes to act as if she were a feminist. Still, they are our cousins."

"Let us not be too critical," his mother remarked. "If young people do not lead the way toward change, who will?"

"Progress isn't *always* good," Chandra answered shortly. He was beginning to feel rather cross with all this business of altering everything. He was satisfied to have things stay as they were. He had guessed for a long time that his mother did not fit into any settled pattern, any old-fashioned pattern. This was the first time that he had noticed that she was ready to evaluate young people on the basis of their progressiveness.

The afternoon the small family party set out in Kumar's car for the Ngong Hills, which were only a few miles from the city, was one of billowing clouds. Peter Hope would have liked it, and Chandra was suddenly reminded of him now.

A dozen or two years ago, the Hills had seemed far enough out to provide one of the most popular hunting grounds for the Europeans of Nairobi. Then the city had not yet spread, and travel out on poor highways had been slow.

The road they were taking climbed steadily upward and soon the city lay below them in the distance. When they stopped, Rosie chose a spot where grass made a smooth carpet and where there was an open view.

Here they were roughly one hundred miles due south of the Equator and about the same distance southeast of Mt. Kenya. More than one hundred and fifty miles slightly east of south from here rose Mt. Kilimanjaro in Tanganyika. Almost as far due west lay Lake Victoria. The Ngong Hills marked the edge of the Great Rift Valley which fell sharply away on their west.

Breezes were coming from the northwest. Today

when these struck the high points of the Hills, they clung there as if caught by a magnet. Instead of dropping their moisture, they were simply soft and beautiful. The clouds which missed the Hills were even more magnificent for they advanced across the sky in an irregular procession, to disappear in the blue beyond. As they went, they were so gay and alive.

"Look, please look," Rosie commanded, watching them. "You will never see anything more beautiful in all the earth than these hills changing shape and color and height with the time of day and the lighting. Nor will you ever see anything as magnificent as the great plains to the south where the animals are. Nor, for that matter, will you ever find anything to match the foothills of the Kikuyu Reserve on the east and north or the deep valley of the Rift with winding dry river beds, mimosa and cactus, to the west." She stopped, suddenly. "I am boring you," she murmured. Yet she was impelled to go on.

"Once buffalo and eland and rhino lived here in the Hills, but now coffee and tea farms have come in and they have fled. Not but that the farms are beautiful—especially when the coffee is in blossom . . . Have you lived in Nairobi and never smelled the bitter fragrance of coffee blossoms? A misty white? Or seen the red berries before the women and children come to pick them? Oh—but I must not go on so—only it is a shame to miss any beauty in the world."

She turned and smiled at the young people who had scattered themselves on the smooth grass and who were looking about them with mild interest. Krishna was a beautiful girl except that she had a discontented face; Kumar gave the impression of already knowing all that the world had to teach. Tom was throwing tiny stones at the target of a small twisted thorn tree down the hillside. Chandra was neatly seated on a stump.

The sun began to sink so soon that they had to hurry with their lunch, for here near the Equator days and nights were always the same length. The beauty grew more intense all the time. Now the Hills were edged with golden light as the sun dropped behind them but seemed to glance upward the more brightly because of that. Soft dusk, a softer feeling than the brilliant day could ever bring, developed slowly and they sat almost silent with their thoughts. Perhaps it was just what they all needed, the mother thought. Surely the young people should be the ones to talk, not she, anyway. But sometimes they seemed to be waiting for her or for someone. She felt it especially now that in the gathering darkness they knew their faces could not be seen and read.

Once more she began to think aloud, invited by their listening silence.

"One reason why I always love to come to the Hills, or go further to where we can look into the Valley of the Rift, is that they remind me of Uganda," she said, thoughtfully. "The Ruwenzori Mountains, or the Mountains of the Moon, rise in the western part of that country. No white man ever climbed them until Henry Stanley did in 1875—so the histories say that they were not discovered until then."

A slight sound came from Kumar's direction. He was only shifting his position. "The white man is the only human being who ever discovered anything, as far as histories are concerned," he remarked.

The East African Office, London

Lake Bunyonyi, Uganda.

"Of course those mountains are hard to climb because they are forever smothered in clouds for the atmosphere is hot there and mists form around the cold peaks . . . Lake Victoria bounds Uganda on the south, the second largest lake in the world. It was also discovered by the white man and properly measured and recorded by him." She fell silent before she started on again. "Crocodiles and hippos live there and it is not much good to people because it makes them sick with bilharzia. Yet Entebbe, the capital the British built, is very near the lake."

"It has the best airport in Africa, or one of the best," Chandra filled in.

Quietness fell over the group. Overhead the first stars were appearing and in Nairobi the street lights went on, making it look far more cosmopolitan than it really was. They ought to be going home because of biting insects, but they were all used to the life, and so they did not hurry, but again waited for Rosie to speak.

"You are all part of the family, my family," she went on carefully, "whether my children, or my husband's brother's children. I have come to a time when I want to tell you a bit of our history of which I am proud and which I think you ought to know, in this day and time. It may help to explain why I do not always behave quite as other Indian women behave in our community."

She paused again. A figure rose and moved. Then Tom was standing near her, one foot on a clump of grass or something, leaning forward as if protecting her. Chandra was tense, glad that it was almost dark. He believed that the cousins were not paying very close attention. They probably thought that their aunt had always been an odd one, anyway, too independent and undignified.

"I am speaking of Uganda because I come from there," she said, clearly. "Sudar was there for a time as a young man, connected with the cloth industry before he took up tailoring, and we became acquainted —one might say indirectly as was customary then. There are many Indians in Uganda and my father was one of them. My mother," her words seemed more distinct than usual, "belonged to the Baganda tribe, and so I am half African." She turned toward all of them, and they could feel her smiling in her warm, outgoing way.

"The Baganda are that great tribe that I have learned about in school," Tom put in eagerly. " 'Progressive, proud, democratic. Their government was well-organized even before any explorer reached them' —that's a quote!" The boy's voice was strong and defiant. He did not give his mother time to say anything but went on quickly. He had read about these people only a short time ago and it was all fresh in his mind. "Their history goes back to a thousand years before Jesus . . . They wear clothes of beautifully dyed bark cloth."

"They are impulsive, quick to humor, and quick of temper," Rosie added, taking up her son's manner. "Once a group of page boys in the royal court became

Christians and the dreadful young king, Mwanga, ordered them put to death unless they renounced their religion. He waited for ten days, and when they would not deny their faith, he had them burned at the stake— all but one whose name is Ham Mukasa. If you go there you can see the stone crosses that mark the place where the thirty-two were put to death." She waited. No one spoke. They had all heard about this historical event, but it had been impersonal before.

"We must go home," Rosie said, quietly. As they got up, Tom was beside her helping her over the rough places which were hard to see now. Just behind was Chandra and she waited for him to say something. But he said nothing. Krishna and Kumar began chattering about the city lights and a coming concert.

When they had reached the car, Chandra was glad that the interior bulb did not work. They roared into the short drive home.

Rosie was engulfed in sadness and remorse because of what she had told. Had she misjudged the young people? Her own sons? Not Tom. She could almost feel him reaching out to her. Still, she was not going to let herself regret having spoken as she had. Her mixed blood had stood like a shadow in her life all through the years when she had been waiting for her sons to grow up. She believed that they were grown now and that their cousins, behind all their front of unyielding modernity, were sensible and broad-minded.

But when they left they only said their good nights, politely, at the Mookerji door. Perhaps they were embarrassed or uncertain, yet, just how to react. Let time pass, she told herself.

Once they were indoors, Chandra confronted his mother, his rare anger blazing. "Why did you have to tell us?" he demanded harshly. Boro, who had run in to see if she could bring her mistress anything, disappeared hastily.

"Because you, too, are partly Baganda—or Kiganda, as the adjective is," she answered firmly. "When one has become a man, one should know one's heritage. You have every reason to be proud of yours."

"*I* am," Tom said, coming to stand straight and tall before her. "I am African, anyway. So are you, Chandra. We live in Africa—why not have the best African blood in our veins? Do we need to apologize for our mother—I mean our grandmother?"

Chandra raised his hand and studied it. It looked so Indian, for it was small-boned and delicate. Yet through its veins, he knew now, African blood was flowing. It would take him a long time to get used to that.

But his sense of decency soon came back steadily. He looked at his mother and was shocked to see her eyes bright with quick, sad tears. So many moments out of the past came flashing back in that instant— all the years since his father had died when she had done everything she could to make their life full and happy; her continual great good humor; her little plans for fun together. She was just herself; no one could

Baganda mother and child, Uganda.

ever be like her. It could not matter what her blood was.

He struggled to speak, to say something to make her feel better—but the right words would not come. They still held complaint.

"Why did you have to tell us this in front of our cousins? Now they will tell everyone."

"They are part of our family. They will tell no one except members of the family to which they, also, belong. It was time to tell it, now that you are grown."

They had all been standing in a kind of frozen stage act. Now Rosie dropped slowly into a chair and the boys sat down, too.

"It's okay with me," Tom said, sturdily. "I guess I'd better get some homework done—maybe more about the Baganda," he added grinning at them both before he went to another room.

Chandra went to his mother. "I hope you won't think too badly of me," he whispered. "I'm rather ashamed of myself . . . You know, I really feel we couldn't have had a better mother." His words were stiff and halting, but as he started away he stooped and rested his face against her hair. Rosie sat without moving. It was the rarest of gestures for her son, Chandra. This was the second happiest moment of her life. The first had been the one when young Sudar Mookerji had asked her father if she could become his wife.

CHAPTER 11

I T WAS hard for Chandra to accept the fact that he was not pure Indian, and yet, in some strange way, it set him free. He began to be more aware of movements that were going on around him. Before, he had drawn back, afraid of whatever might bring change. Now he found the thought of it rather inviting and challenging.

He had always looked at all African countries, even Kenya, from outside, clinging to its British or its Indian aspects. He was now beginning to face the fact that Africa was African. But he was not ready to admit to any new point of view, yet.

Perhaps the fact that his people had come to Africa from another country was what made any kind of patriotism so hard for him and for some of his friends. To what country were they supposed to be patriotic?

He had always thought of his father as one patriotic to India—that India of ancient cultures and of Gandhi who had used age-old techniques of nonresistance based on religious feeling. He had thought of his mother as patriotic to Indian Kenya.

When he thought more about her, at home or at work, after the evening in the Hills, he realized that she was patriotic in a very broad way. "She'd be patriotic to any country that she lived in!" he put it to himself, smiling suddenly.

Well, his cousins were just trying to pull in two directions at once, he decided. They were trying to be properly British-Indian, and still liberal, modern young people. One might have been both only a few years ago, but it no longer seemed possible. A man either clung to the past and remained with his origins, or let go of them entirely to become himself in a new world. At least that was the way it seemed to him.

Chandra realized that his own attitude was changing. His cousins were the first to notice it. Though the three of them had rarely done the same things before, now they sometimes found themselves together unexpectedly.

Once it was at a meeting of a society for cultural co-operation. The society was working for a closer relationship between eastern and central African countries. It stood against white supremacy, but for European culture. Membership was open to Africans, Asians and Europeans.

"What—you here, too!" Kumar said in surprise when he came face to face with Chandra for the first time at one of the meetings. Krishna's eyes, too, showed astonishment.

"I could say the same to you," Chandra laughed.

"But why have you said nothing about this? I suppose you thought I would not be interested—and it is the first time for me."

"Well, I've only come out of curiosity," Kumar answered, quickly nonchalant.

"We are all hurrying to excuse ourselves for being interested in mixing cultures," Krishna said in her downright way. "I am here because this organization is supposed to be devoted to the westernization of the people of Africa. That makes much more sense than talk of mixing the races." Today she looked stunning in a western dress that still used the brilliant colors of India.

"Krishna worships anything that is western or, rather, modern," Kumar teased. "If it's modern, it's okay, as far as she is concerned." He fell in beside Chandra as the three walked into the large hall where a crowd was gathering.

"Seriously," he said in a low tone, looking around, "I don't know whether it is a good thing to come to these meetings, or not. One never knows about these organizations. Are they for racial intermarriage, Communistic, or something?"

"We shall find out," Chandra answered. He was secretly annoyed at the question. "I would say, first of all, that this one, at least, is a patriotic organization."

But what was patriotism in Africa? To what or to whom was one patriotic? To India, Britain, Kenya? To the Kikuyu tribe? To the Mau Mau movement? Patriotism had no meaning unless it was strong

161

enough to demand work and loyalty from one. Chandra thought it over slowly, trying to decide just what patriotism should require of a person like himself. He had never even thought about it until now, for he had always believed that he was too far from India even to concern himself with such a question.

Now as they took seats, he noticed that people were grouping, by habit, in nationality sections. Krishna sat between the two young men, as if protected from any neighbors . . . It suddenly came to Chandra that he and his cousins were together as naturally as though his mother had never said anything about her heritage the other evening . . . But all three of them were a little ill at ease, watching what was going on around them now and wondering.

Kumar did not seem to be able to keep quiet tonight. He began talking again during the murmur made by the gathering audience. "A great example of patriotism, not based on any oneness of origin, is, of course, the United States of America," he announced.

"You have to leave people of African origin out of that statement, partly, at least," Krishna said shortly. "The black skin is not fully a part of even your wonderful example." She seemed to get some comfort out of that thought.

"Not because *they* are not patriotic," Chandra found himself saying with some heat. "I've read of how loyal they were during the wars." He hesitated and then went on, though as he did so he suddenly asked himself whether this was he speaking or Sudar, his father, through him. "There is a new kind of patriotism developing over there among the Negroes—new for America, that is. It's to be found in the sit-ins against discrimination. Dr. Martin Luther King, a Negro minister, seems to be a fine example of it."

"I must say I wouldn't call that patriotism," Kumar remarked dryly. "They're just trying to get what they want, and that's the easiest way to do it—no bloodshed, no anything except some free food and lodging in jail."

"Oh, now, Kumar," Krishna protested, turning dark angry eyes toward him. "That's a beastly way to put it!"

"Well—how would *you* put it?" he demanded, his eyes flaming, too.

She hesitated and then began, carefully.

"I think they are right in thinking that they have been wronged. They are citizens of the United States and, on the books, equal treatment is rightfully theirs. They are not getting it and they are sincere in trying to get it. They know it can never be done by fighting because they are a minority. This nonviolent method is about the only one a minority has . . . Now over here it is very different. The blacks are colonial subjects of Britain. They haven't the basis to demand equality because they jolly well aren't equal, even on the books."

"And *we* haven't some rights, either— Why? Because we aren't equal to the British? Is that what you are saying?" Kumar demanded of Krishna.

"Hush— The meeting is beginning," Chandra

163

whispered. They sat back in the seats and listened.

The leader was also the chairman of the Nairobi section of the society. It was not easy to tell what his background was, but Chandra guessed after a time that it was originally Indian. The members of the Executive Committee who were sitting on the platform with him ranged from vivid black to European white.

The atmosphere of the meeting was stimulating. In spite of themselves, the young people were affected by it as the evening went on. Speakers were taking different points of view for granted. Some of them were ideas which Chandra was just beginning to think about or was struggling over—the coming independence of East Africa; modernization of a multiracial society without discrimination, and with, astonishingly, a Christian religious background. Did they mean Christian as a way of behaving or Christian in a formal sense? They were often different, he knew.

One speaker after another got up and addressed them, explaining the purposes of the society. Questions from the floor followed. Phrases like Pan-Africanism, which meant throwing out all colonial rule, All-African People's Organization, which seemed to be a nongovernmental movement of nationalist parties, the Afro-Asian Solidarity Movement, United States of West Africa—and, it seemed, a dozen others were tossed about. The young people saw that they had really been half-asleep while others in Africa had been trying to achieve freedom and workable political machinery.

The United Nations was mentioned most often of all. Chandra had a growing feeling that it was a stage on which new nations made their bow to the world before they took up their responsibilities.

But Kenya was not among those who had yet stepped upon that stage, nor was Uganda, nor Tanganyika. Still, one speaker pointed out, by the end of 1960 nearly two-thirds of Africa's people would be independent. Living in East Africa it was hard to realize that so much was happening.

The whole meeting was bewildering—yet wonderful. For it showed that change was possible and that it was inevitably coming. It put independence within reach. It suggested that barriers between countries and nationalities could be broken down.

When Chandra glanced at Krishna once or twice during the evening, he saw that she was listening raptly. Kumar was paying close attention, too, though he pretended disinterest.

At last the meeting was over. The crowd dispersed almost silently. The young people themselves parted with no more than a good night. They were not ready to show their feelings; they were even uncertain what they were.

CHAPTER 12

ONE morning Chandra was astonished to receive a letter from Jim Smith who was again in the United States. He used the first free moment he had to read it. How like his old friend it sounded! The picture of the American group came back clearly.

"I want you to get acquainted with one of my professors, Sam Horn, who is going to East Africa," Jim wrote. "He is a sociologist and you will like him. He plans to be in the area for several months, studying some group, I think, the Kikuyu. He also wants to meet people in Nairobi, of course."

Chandra read on, growing excited and then beginning to have misgivings. A sociologist from America? A professor? He did not feel prepared to meet or to help such a person. Yet it was nice to know that Jim had thought of him. He would do whatever he could to be useful.

Perhaps it would be a good idea for him to find

out more about the people of Tanganyika, Kenya and Uganda himself, before Mr. Horn arrived. He had lived his own Indian life without paying much attention to other groups. This was what most people did.

Tanganyika, like Kenya, was populated by Bantu tribes which included the Kikuyu, by Asians, and by Europeans. But only about 16,000 Kikuyu lived here while more than one million lived in Kenya. The proportions of Asians and Europeans in Tanganyika were considerably smaller than in Kenya, although both states had large areas which had been taken entirely over by white settlers.

The Masai were an important non-Bantu group. There were thought to be 45,000 of them in Tanganyika and 60,000 in Kenya. The Masai were herdsmen who roamed the plains and lived on milk and on blood drawn from their cattle. They had once been fierce, proud warriors. Now they seemed to be less interested in nationalism than many other tribal groups in Africa.

The next largest group of tribespeople in Tanganyika were the Sukuma. They were forward-looking and particularly interested in improving their agricultural methods.

As Chandra tried to inform himself, he was brought back again and again to the Kikuyu people. They were already so familiar to him, so much his neighbors, that he had never thought about them particularly before. Now he was discovering that they had had a unique history.

In ancient times the Kikuyu had had no chiefs.

When the British started to work with them they tried to institute a system of chieftains so that they would have responsible leaders to negotiate with. For a long time they were unsuccessful for the Kikuyu had a rather democratic social system based on age groups, and they did not want to change it.

But at the time when the British East Africa Company was organized, the Kikuyu people were having a desperate period of drought, of animal and human disease, as well as an invasion of locusts. They had had to desert great areas of land temporarily. It was splendid land, high and fertile. It was also so located geographically that many English crops would grow there, while tea and coffee would also produce well.

Believing that these Bantu people did not claim to own land, British settlers began to take possession of it, either outright or on a long lease basis. Lands that were appropriated in this way were called Crown Land. Usually payment of some kind was made to the Kikuyu for it, but what the British did not realize was that lands could not be so easily bought among these tribespeople. Complicated ceremonies of which the British knew nothing at all had to be connected with any actual transfer of property. The British were not interested in learning the Kikuyu language, much less in trying to understand any involved tribal customs.

Swahili, a language made up of an Arabic word construction and Bantu grammar was the East African language most commonly learned by Europeans. It was the one which Chandra used when he spoke to Africans. But the Kikuyu spoke something entirely different and only a handful of Europeans had learned anything about it.

Rosie's maid, Boro, was a Kikuyu for her people learned quickly and were dependable. They were known to be clever and industrious. It was they who became the workers on the railroads, who were the artisans, the servants and chaffeurs. They were always eager to go to school whenever they possibly could.

Now their old village life had largely broken up. Many families lived near towns and had small houses like those in any modern country. Usually at least one member of a family worked in town to earn cash. He brought back a taste for new things and an ambition to change the way of life. This mixture of old and new was to be seen everywhere among the Kikuyu.

The terrorist society called Mau Mau was largely made up of Kikuyu people. It was bitterly opposed to white men in Africa. Though it may have started because the tribe was wronged by the British, either through lack of understanding or because of methods that were too aggressive, it was also a result of the breakdown of tribal customs. No new rules about how to live had yet been set up to replace old ones which could no longer be followed.

Even the Mau Mau were only another sign of the troubling question that had to be answered. How were Europeans, Asians and Africans going to live together on this great continent? Until an answer was found, Kenya would not be able to industrialize. Unless she industrialized she could not produce enough to meet the needs of her people. Yet she did not have capital to invest in such industries. If times were unsettled, no one from outside wanted to put large sums of capital into the country, for fear of losing them. The problem became clearer and more difficult as Chandra went into it. His own people, the Indians, had been shrewd and aggressive. They had come off well in the economy they controlled. He saw that they had had little concern for how the Africans came off in the business.

All around Nairobi stretched what were known as the "white highlands," areas that had been given to or taken by European settlers. To the north, the east and the south were the Native Land Units. Those of the Kikuyu were to the northeast, those of the Masai to the west and the south.

South of Nairobi geographically lay the Athi Plains. Beyond them rose Mt. Kilimanjaro, a mile higher than any point in the United States of America, higher than Mt. Blanc or the Jungfrau in Switzerland. It seemed even higher than it was because it towered above plains rather than foothills. Though only about two hundred miles from the Equator, it was always covered with snow. When the monsoon clouds from the Indian Ocean struck its sides, rains came. Its snows melted to form streams and rivers which watered fine garden lands at its base.

When Chandra turned his thoughts to Uganda, his feelings changed. Perhaps this was because his mother had so often told Tom and him about it. Although there were three other major kingdoms, always the

170

Baganda people dominated the story. He saw the dignified robes of the men, the bright flowing dresses of the women. He was aware of Makerere College, of the capital cities of Kampala and Entebbe. There was the marvelous lake; the source of the Nile.

One important historical fact was that white people had not been allowed to own land. This meant that Uganda had avoided many problems connected with white settlements. For example, the color bar, or discrimination on the basis of race, was much weaker here than where there were white settlers.

Because of the search for the source of the River Nile, Uganda had become a dramatic spot in the world. She still had something of that drama for her lands were rich, her people, led by the Baganda, self-assertive, and her life somehow gay and colorful. Now as Chandra looked at it more objectively than ever before, he easily saw why his mother was the person she was. Though she was part African and his father had been Indian, he could imagine that she had felt a certain condescension when she married the little cloth merchant. After all, he smiled to himself, her mother had been a Baganda!

Often he thought about India while he reviewed and added to his knowledge of East Africa. The British had trained an Indian leadership in his country before they left—or were pushed out. Were they preparing African leaders for East Africa in the same way? He did not believe that Kenya was being made ready for the change as India had been. And even he knew that the leaders in the new government would

171

have to be African Africans and not Indian Africans or European Africans. The trouble was that there was still a feeling abroad that Africans could not govern in modern ways.

What would Professor Samuel Horn think about it all? This question was enough to make Chandra await his arrival uneasily, yet with great excitement.

CHAPTER 13

W HY was he who had never been to what the Americans called a college so involved in this business of Professor Horn's coming, Chandra sometimes asked himself. He even complained to his mother about it.

"You know very well it is because of Jim Smith," she said downrightly. "He wants his teacher to have friends here. I suppose that the Americans became better acquainted with us than with any other Kenyans during the short time that they were in the city."

As for Rosie Mookerji, she looked forward to the professor's coming with enormous interest. If he was going to study the peoples here, she was going to find out what his opinions of them were, and also discover more about the United States of America.

What was a sociologist, anyway? She looked up the word in the worn English dictionary which Sudar had bought for Chandra years ago. "One who specializes in the study of origins, development, organization and functioning of human society," it said. She would never have even tried to pronounce the long words, but she could guess their meaning.

After a good deal of thought she boiled them down to something much simpler. "One who studies people and how they behave," Rosie put it to herself. No subject could possibly intrigue her more. She realized in a flash that *she* had been studying it a long time in her own way.

Tom was interested, too, in Professor Horn's coming, although he did not pretend interest in the reason for it. As far as he was concerned, people were just people and there was not much use in analyzing them. Still, he sometimes thought of Hubertus.

He was having a great time in sports at school this year as captain of the junior rugby team and as a member of the cricket team. The Indian school which he attended was patterned after those of England and some of its graduates went on to a university. The Africans had nothing like it although thousands were in elementary schools and several hundred were in intermediate or secondary schools which had both Christian mission and colonial government support.

Even though they had thought so much about his coming, the Mookerji family was astonished to open the door late on a Sunday afternoon and find the tall, bespectacled American standing before them. He could not possibly have fitted their imagined picture of Professor Samuel Horn better than he did.

"This must be Chandra Mookerji's mother," he said easily, holding out a long hand, "and Chandra, and—let me see—Tom." He smiled triumphantly at them all.

"Please come in, Professor Horn," Rosie said with the little air she put on sometimes. "We have looked forward to your arrival with the keenest anticipation."

Chandra was amused by his mother, in spite of his real interest in the American. He glanced quickly from her to Mr. Horn as they sat down. Boro peeped around a corner, her eyes widening in open astonishment, before she went quickly to prepare English tea. When she reappeared with it, Chandra noticed that the sociologist was studying her and probably making mental notes.

Meantime, he was explaining his reasons for coming in a rather simple, pleasant way. Certainly he was not awesome or frightening. In fact, one almost forgot that he was such a scholar.

"I am sure you are wondering about people like me," he said, stretching his long legs out before him and then drawing them up again and crossing them instead, when he saw the floor space he was taking. "I suppose we're a queer lot because our work has only begun and it hasn't much history, yet."

"I shouldn't think it would have to prove itself by a history," Rosie said, remembering the definition of sociologist. "Nothing could be more important than people and how they behave!"

Her sons stared at her, astounded. She seemed to

know all about this man's work! They never could be altogether sure just what she was about.

Sam Horn looked across at the plump little woman and noted her sparkling eyes and alert expression. Here was someone who might introduce him to a variety of people and might also have some pretty good observations of her own. He would ask her about contacts in and around Nairobi when they were better acquainted.

"Well," he went on now, picking up the thread of conversation, "I suppose that one could say that the sociologist would like to be considered a scientist who is concerned with human society. But science is something that can be measured and calculated so as to come out with an answer, and human beings cannot be used in such an exact way—at least, not yet. They keep escaping, reaching back into the past, forming new combinations, and so on. One cannot separate them out." He shook his head and studied the toe of one shoe. He was sure that he was not making sense to his audience. He must watch himself and keep on the level of those with whom he talked.

"Of course," Rosie said quite cheerfully. "Tribal people have known that a long time. Tribes are made up of the dead as well as of the living. Isn't that part of what you were saying?" She flashed sparkling eyes at him.

"Exactly!" he answered, smiling around at all three of them. "I hope that I meet up with such understanding elsewhere, Mrs. Mookerji." He turned to the boys and began to ask them about work and school.

"You've been graduated quite a long time then, Chandra—I hope you don't mind my being so familiar. That was the way Jim always referred to you—and Americans are so bad about formalities."

Chandra had actually been thinking that he did not particularly care for the fact that this stranger had addressed him by his first name at the door, but now he put this lack of courtesy down to the American uncouthness. He really liked the man enormously, already, and knew him to be warm and understanding.

"I finished school a little more than two years ago," he answered the implied question. "I am doing what I have always planned to do. I shall be promoted to higher ranks at the proper time, if all goes well." He found himself ready to defend his job and his life plan. He knew that Americans were all for going to school no end and then, perhaps, not knowing what they wanted to do next. At least, that was the way it had sometimes seemed to him. They were ready to free the world, only, they had a hard time deciding how they were going to go about it. He knew what he was going to do, step by step, and year by year.

"I am sure you must like your work or you wouldn't be so enthusiastic about your plans," Sam Horn said, shifting his position easily . . . "Tell me about Nairobi. Why do the different peoples still live so separately? Why is there such strong feeling between the Africans and the Asians? If it isn't color—and can it be when neither is white—then what is it? When did it begin? When did your family come to Kenya? Has its social position changed?"

177

He laughed aloud and took off his glasses, polished them hard and then put them on again. "Don't answer any of those questions. They are samples, only probably more direct, of the kinds I shall be asking. Actually I shan't be able to ask many questions myself because I am illiterate in anything but English so I shall have to find local people to help me." His blue eyes gleamed and Chandra had the impression that he was looking forward to it all with great relish.

"It will not be easy to answer some of those," he said thoughtfully. "One scarcely knows why one's grandparents came, nor why they stayed."

"To build the railroads," Tom put in unexpectedly. "The railroad *made* Nairobi and Kenya. Mother, isn't that so?" He might have heard it from Sudar, his father, but he must have been too young to remember much that went back that far.

"It is so," she answered promptly.

She had heard it explained many times. West Africa was opened to European trade long before East Africa because, until the Suez Canal was dug, East Africa was so much harder to reach.

When the British East Africa Company decided to come in, they were really aiming at Uganda rather that at what is now Kenya. For the Nile had always been a mystery. In 1854 a man named Speke discovered that it began at Lake Victoria. He and others who followed him in were astonished at some of the people they found there, especially the Baganda. They were even more impressed by their kings, first Mutesa and then his son, Mwanga. The kingdom of the Ba-

178

ganda, called Buganda, was surprisingly rich and well-organized, if lacking in humanitarian principles. Soon traders and missionaries wanted to enter. There had to be an easier way to get in. The railroad was planned, but it was a dreadful undertaking.

Building of the railroad started in 1895. The line had to begin at the town of Mombasa, on the coast, go through wild territory to the inland highlands which reached an altitude of 7,000 feet, go down 1,500 feet again to pass through the Rift Valley, then up once more to the Kikuyu lands which stood at 8,500, and then down to the lake. Thirty-two thousand Indians were brought across the Indian Ocean to do the work. Sudar's parents and her own father had been among them.

They had faced such dreadful hardships as disease and attacks by wild animals. When in 1899 the track had reached the point where Nairobi stands, three hundred and thirty miles from Mombasa, the hardest part was over. There were still more than five hundred miles to cover before they would come to Kampala in Uganda.

"Why didn't they use local Africans?" Sam Horn interrupted to ask, not because he did not have one answer but because he wanted to see if an additional one would be given.

"They didn't know how to do the work," Chandra explained quietly. "They had no idea what a railroad track was supposed to be, or what a train was."

"And did the Indians who had been brought over from their villages?"

"Most of them did. They had come part way to the ships by rail." Chandra felt himself on guard for an argument, but he must avoid that.

"You have lived in or near Nairobi ever since?" Sam Horn covered them all in his question.

"Yes," Rosie answered, "except that my husband was in Uganda as a young man for a time and then returned here."

"I see," the American said, thoughtfully.

Soon he thanked them and left for his hotel for it was growing late.

This was the first of many visits. Chandra learned that Sam Horn was gathering a group of workers to collect statistics for him, training them first so that they would know how to do what he wanted. Chandra learned, too, that he was a man who was highly respected in his field; that he was connected with universities in both the United States and Africa. Yet when he came to the Mookerji house, he seemed so unscholarly and so humble that both the young men became very fond of him. They talked more frankly with him than with the other Americans, while Rosie looked on, pleased that this man was their friend for even so short a time. He thought freely about everything, and she believed that this attitude might help Chandra. Tom was clearly already open to any possibility for himself. But Chandra—Chandra was just an old-fashioned Indian when it came to his work, she decided.

Month passed month and still Sam Horn stayed in

Nairobi or else went away into some remote part of East Africa, then returned to work up his material.

The day he was to leave came at last. It was spring 1961 and the time of the great rains. Rosie always enjoyed the swirling monsoon clouds, the torrents, the rushing street ditches, the gurgling house gutters—and then the sudden break in the clouds which brought a short pause. Sam Horn had come to say good-by. If she had known the moment was near, she would have planned a farewell of some kind. There was no time for that. Now he stood there, his raincoat glistening with moisture, before them.

Chandra was sorry to see him leave. It was as though he had opened a window into the world and pointed out a highway which led out to undiscovered lands. Now the window might close, the road disappear. He held his hand out to the American and said suddenly, "Thank you for—" he hesitated in a confusion that was rare for him, and at last went on slowly, "—all you've told us about." It was not what he wanted to say, at all, but he could not put it into words.

They gripped hands and then the American, not looking at him but at some cards he had taken from a pocket, said in an offhand way, "There's nothing to thank me for . . . If, after a time, you think that you'd like some more education, write to me here. I'll be back in the States in another two months. I could probably get a scholarship for you either in a technical school or in a regular college, if you decide you are interested. Of course I don't need to tell you, I'd recommend the college because it would open more doors."

"Say—Chandra! How about that! Great, I'd say!" The words burst from Tom.

"I'd have to think it over," Chandra said very slowly. "But I *am* grateful, awfully grateful, Mr. Horn." By now his face was flushed with high color, and the hand which received the address card from Sam Horn was noticeably trembling.

Rosie said good-by to their friend, her eyes glowing as he looked into them. He guessed at her appreciation for the offer to help Chandra but there was no time left to talk about it. He had known that it would not do to make the offer too early in his visit although he had recognized Chandra's ability very soon. Shaking Tom's hand, too, he turned and left, racing for his car in a shower.

Rosie Mookerji knew better than to add anything to what had already been said. She simply closed the door and went to the kitchen to see what Boro and the other servants were about. But the men of the family were thinking deeply of the man who had walked into their lives and then out again.

Tom threw himself into a chair and stared straight ahead, his face alight, a half-smile still on his face, his long legs stretched almost across the room, it seemed.

Chandra gazed at the streaming panes of the windows, his hands in his pockets, his eyes smoldering. Then he wheeled suddenly around and seeing his brother sitting so, said sharply, "Tom, for decency's sake, do stop lounging all over the place like that!" But though his brother obeyed instantly, he guessed Chandra's crossness was only a sign that he was thinking hard about what Mr. Horn had said.

He was right for almost immediately Chandra smiled at him sheepishly and muttered, "I apologize for that beastly way of speaking . . . I say, Tom, if we'd get scholarships and so be able to get better jobs, our mother would be more comfortably off in the end than if we just stuck here, wouldn't she?"

"Of course—and she'd be that *pleased,* she'd not know what to do with herself," Tom almost shouted on the point of leaping from his chair.

"I hadn't thought of all that. *Of course* she would like the idea . . . I think I'll go and talk it with her a bit right now—just sort of open the subject from our side—give it a first going over, you know." He looked hard at Tom seeming to want his clear approval of the plan before he went quickly from the room.

AFRICA

		Area Square Miles	Population	Colonial History	Independence Status 1960	Relation to United Nations
1. The Northwest Territory	Egypt	386,000	22,313,000	British	Independent	Member
	Sudan	967,500	11,549,000	British	Independent	Member
	Libya	697,358	1,200,000	Italian	Independent	Member
	Tunisia	48,319	3,987,000	French	Independent	Member
	Morocco	170,382	10,165,000	Spanish	Independent	Member
	Algeria	919,352	10,648,000	French	Part of France	
	Spanish Sahara	102,255	78,000	Spanish	Colony of Spain	
2. West Africa	Mauritania	419,390	685,000	French	Independent	
	Gambia	3,978	307,000	British	Colony of Britain	
	Mali Republic	405,050	3,748,000	French	Independent	Member
	Guinea	94,945	2,667,000	French	Independent	Member
	Portuguese Guinea	13,944	563,000	Portuguese	Part of Portugal	
	Sierra Leone	27,925	2,185,000	British	Colony of Britain	
	Liberia	42,898	1,350,000	———	Independent	Member

Region	Country	Area	Population	Colonial Power	Status	U.N.
West Africa (cont'd)	Upper Volta	105,879	3,516,000	French	Independent	Member
	Ivory Coast	124,550	3,145,000	French	Independent	Member
	Ghana	91,819	4,847,000	British	Independent	Member
	Togoland	22,000	1,136,000	British	Independent	Member
	Dahomey	44,713	1,750,000	French	Independent	Member
	Nigeria	350,291	33,441,000	British	Independent	Member
	Niger	459,180	2,515,000	French	Independent	Member
	Cameroons Republic	166,252	3,303,000	French	Independent	Member
	Spanish Guinea	10,828	216,000	Spanish	Colony of Spain	
3. Equatorial Africa	Gabon	98,283	434,400	French	Independent	Member
	Congo Republic	125,890	816,000	French	Independent	Member
	Chad	466,640	2,541,000	French	Independent	Member
	Central African Republic	277,118	1,224,000	French	Independent	Member
	Angola	481,226	4,496,000	Portuguese	Part of Portugal	
	Belgian Congo	905,329	13,732,000	Belgian	Independent	Member
	Ruanda-Urundi	30,916	4,941,000	Belgian	Belgian	U.N. Trust Territory
4. Horn of Africa	Ethiopia	457,147	21,351,000	Independent	Independent	Member
	Somalia	178,155	1,367,000	Italian	Independent	Member

	Area Square Miles	Population	Colonial History	Independence Status 1960	Relation to United Nations
Horn of Africa (cont'd)					
French Somaliland	8,492	69,300	French	Colony France	
5. East Africa					
Kenya	224,960	6,444,000	British	Colony of Britain	
Uganda	93,981	5,592,000	British	British Protectorate	
Tanganyika	362,688	9,052,000	British	U.N. Trust Territory	
Mozambique	279,654	6,253,000	Portuguese	Part of Portugal	
6. Central Africa Federation					
Southern Rhodesia	150,327	2,664,000	British	British Self-Governing Colony	
Northern Rhodesia	284,745	2,325,000	British	British Protectorate	
Nyasaland	37,374	2,267,000	British	British Protectorate	

Region	Territory	Area	Colonial Power	Status
7. Southern Africa	Union of South Africa	472,550	British	Independent Member British Commonwealth Member
	Southwest Africa	317,725	German	Mandated territory Union of South Africa
8. High Commission Territories	Basutoland	11,716	British	Colony of Britain
	Bechuanaland	274,928	British	British Protectorate
	Swaziland	6,705	British	British Protectorate
9. The Islands	Madagascar – Republic of Malagasy	228,510	French	Independent Republic Member
	Mauritius			
	St. Helena			
	Cape Verde Islands			
	Sao Thome and Principe			
	Zanzibar			

ASIA

	Area Square Miles	Population	Colonial History	Independence Status	Relation to United Nations
Burma	261,689	20,303,000	British	Independent Republic	Member
Cambodia	67,550	5,056,000	French	Independent Kingdom	Member
China	3,767,751	699,966,000		Communist Republic	
Formosa	13,885	10,323,000	Japanese	Independent Republic	Member
Hong Kong	391	2,887,000	British	Colony of Britain	
India	1,269,506	404,333,000	British	Independent Republic	Member
Indonesia	575,893	87,802,000	Dutch	Independent Republic	Member
Japan	142,773	93,031,000		Independent Empire	Member
Korea North	47,811	8,083,000	Japanese	Communist Republic	

Korea South	37,414	22,834,000	Japanese	Independent Republic	
Laos	91,482	1,754,000	French	Independent Kingdom	Member
Macao	6.2	228,000	Portuguese	Territory of Portugal	
Malaya	50,677	6,809,000	British	Independent Republic	Member
Mongolia	590,966	1,056,000		Communist Republic	
Nepal	54,330	8,978,000		Independent Kingdom	Member
Pakistan	364,702	86,733,000	British	Independent Republic	Member
Philippines	115,600	23,721,000	Spanish, American	Independent Republic	Member
Singapore	224.5	1,595,000	British	Colony of Britain	
Thailand	198,404	22,003,000		Independent Kingdom	Member
Vietnam North	61,516	14,788,000	French	Communist Republic	
Vietnam South	65,709	12,988,000	French	Independent Republic	

Bibliography

Callis, Vincent, *China, Confucian and Communist*. New York, Henry Holt and Company, 1959.

Cressy, George B., *The Land of the Five Hundred Million*. New York, McGraw-Hill, 1955.

Leakey, L. S. B., *Mau Mau and the Kikuyu*. New York, The John Day Company, 1954.

Moorehead, Alan, *The White Nile*. New York, Harper and Brothers, 1960.

Moon, Parker T., *Imperialism and World Politics*. New York, The Macmillan Company, 1926.

Panikkar, K. M., *The Afro-Asian States and Their Problems*. New York, The John Day Company, 1959.

———, *Asia and Western Dominance*. New York, The John Day Company, 1954.

Payne, Robert, *The Revolt of Asia*. New York, The John Day Company, 1947.

Sithole, Ndabaningi, *African Nationalism*. Oxford University Press (Capetown), 1947.

Also for Further Reading

Dinesen, Isak, *Out of Africa*. New York, Random House, 1960, also, *Shadows on the Grass*. New York, Random House, 1961.

Gunther, John, *Inside Africa*. New York, Harper and Brothers, 1953, 1954, 1955.

Ojike, Mbonu, *My Africa*. New York, The John Day Company, 1946.

Sheean, Vincent, *Nehru, the Years of Power*. New York, Random House, 1960.

Shepherd, George W., Jr., *They Wait in Darkness*. New York, The John Day Company, 1955.

Van der Post, Laurens, *Venture Into the Interior*. New York, William Morrow Company, 1951.

For Quick Reference

Book of Nations, New York, Rand McNally and Company, 1960.

INDEX